THE GEOGRAPHY
OF COMMUNICATIONS IN
GREAT BRITAIN

UNIVERSITY OF HULL PUBLICATIONS

FFYNNONGROEW, NEAR MOSTYN, FLINTSHIRE

The old cliff-line (left) is fronted by flat deposits at the mouth of the Dee estuary. The main road (A.548) picks its way along the old cliff-base, while the railway finds a satisfactory path along the estuarine margin and sweeps round in a gentle curve to take up another straight alignment along the next section of coast through Prestatyn, the general direction of which is indicated by the line of the dunes. View to the west-north-west.

THE GEOGRAPHY
OF COMMUNICATIONS IN
GREAT BRITAIN

BY

J. H. APPLETON

*Lecturer in Geography
in the University of Hull*

Published for the UNIVERSITY OF HULL *by the*

OXFORD UNIVERSITY PRESS

LONDON   NEW YORK   TORONTO

Oxford University Press, Amen House, London E.C.4

GLASGOW NEW YORK TORONTO MELBOURNE WELLINGTON
BOMBAY CALCUTTA MADRAS KARACHI LAHORE DACCA
CAPE TOWN SALISBURY NAIROBI IBADAN ACCRA
KUALA LUMPUR HONG KONG

First published 1962
Reprinted 1965

Printed lithographically in Great Britain by
Butler & Tanner Ltd, Frome and London

VIA INSPIRATIO MEA

CONTENTS

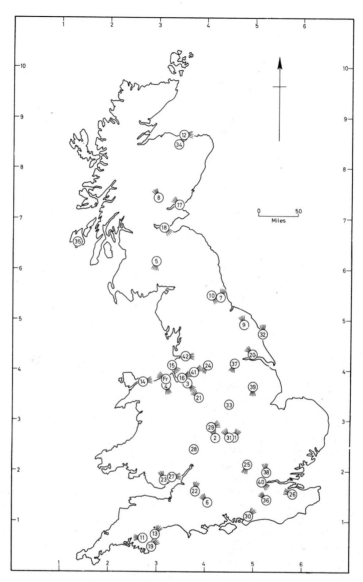

FIG. 1a. LOCATION OF PLATES

The Plate numbers are shown in the circles and the direction of view is
indicated by the rays.

LIST OF PLATES

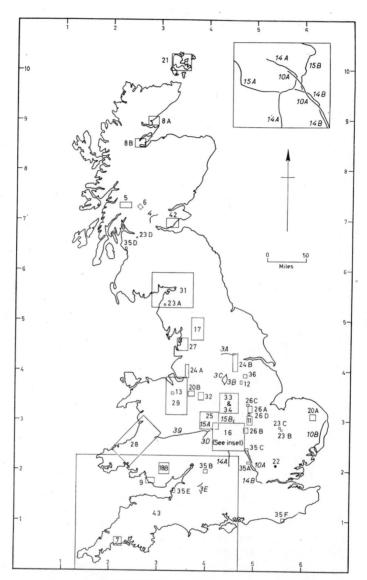

FIG. 1b. LOCATION OF MAPS & DIAGRAMS

The positions of maps are shown by rectangles numbered in upright figures. Sections, gradient profiles, etc., are shown by lines and numbered in italic figures. (See list of maps, diagrams, etc.) The boundaries of the inset are co-extensive with those of Figure 16.

LIST OF MAPS, DIAGRAMS, ETC.

ACKNOWLEDGEMENTS

I acknowledge with thanks information communicated and help given by the Public Relations and Press Officers, Eastern and London Midland Regions, the Chief Civil Engineers, Southern and Scottish Regions, and L. C. Johnson, Esq., Archivist, British Railways; British Transport Waterways, and in particular H. P. Wray, Esq.; the Press Officer, British Transport Commission; S. W. Bainbridge, Esq., Principal Information Officer, and W. F. Adams, Esq., Ministry of Transport and Civil Aviation; the Press and Information Officer, the Gas Council, and C. L. Elliott, Esq.; C. H. Chester, Esq., Chairman, South Western Gas Board; the Air Ministry; the County Surveyor, Lancashire C.C., and the County Road Surveyor, Caithness C.C.; the City Engineer and Surveyor, Nottingham; Harlow Development Corporation; the Scottish Information Office; the County Water Engineer, Lanarkshire C.C. and the Daer Water Board; the General Manager and Secretary, City of Birmingham Water Department; the Engineer and Manager, Manchester Corporation Waterworks; the Tyne Improvement Commission; the Public Relations Officer, British Road Federation; Aerofilms Ltd.; John Laing and Son Ltd.; the Mechanical Engineer, National Coal Board; Mitchell Ropeways Ltd. of Peterborough; British Ropeway Engineering Co. Ltd., London; R. White and Sons (Engineers) Ltd., Widnes; the British Petroleum Co. Ltd.; Kenneth Field, Esq.; Brian Loughbrough, Esq.; Dr. J. K. St. Joseph and the Cambridge University Committee for Aerial Photography; *The Railway Magazine, Geography*, and Professor S. H. Beaver, who have granted permission to use gradient profiles, and the Director-General, Ordnance Survey, who has given permission to print those maps which are based to a greater or lesser extent on Ordnance Survey publications. Specific acknowledgements appear under the maps and plates concerned.

I should also like to record my grateful appreciation of assistance and encouragement received from Dr. L. Dudley Stamp, C.B.E., and from the late Professor H. King, and to express my thanks to Professor H. R. Wilkinson for valuable help in the preparation of the maps and in many other ways. I am greatly indebted also to George de Boer, Alan Harris and Professor S. H. Beaver who have kindly read the manuscript and made valuable suggestions, many of which are incorporated in the following pages.

To Mr. R. Dean I am particularly grateful, not only for his competence in drawing all the maps, but for his inexhaustible patience. I have received assistance of one kind or another from many others, including Mr. Brian Fisher, Miss J. Bailey, Richard Appleton and, last but not least, my wife, to whom I dedicate this book.

INTRODUCTION

Before embarking on a geographical study of communications in Britain, it will be as well to clarify the meaning of a phrase compounded of so many ambiguous terms. 'The two essential questions that the geographer must ask', says J. B. Mitchell,[1] 'are "where?" in order to find out how things are arranged in his place, and then "why there?" in order to appreciate the arrangement that he has found.' Much paper and ink has been used—some would say wasted—in attempting a definition of geography, and it will be much simpler and just as effective to leave the task of definition to others and proceed in the spirit of Miss Mitchell's dictum.

Communications are the channels by which people or things can be moved between places. The term is often extended to cover verbal and even visual messages, from semaphore to television, but these interpretations will not be dealt with in the present context. It must be understood also that the term here refers to internal communications, and that sea transport, even coastal shipping, will not be dealt with. This may not be logical, but the inclusion of such a wide subject would bring in other issues which could not be adequately treated in the space available. Finally the field of investigation will be confined to the mainland of Great Britain with its adjacent islands, but not Ireland. Very likely this is not logical either.

Communications seem to be the Cinderella of geographers. They are always accorded lip-service in theoretical discussion and their importance is invariably acknowledged in regional descriptions. But few geographers have set themselves the task of examining communications for their own sake. Historians and economists have been more active in this field and some admirable studies of communications treated from the historical and economic standpoint are available. They are concerned respectively with how communications came into existence and how they operate in the way of business, and are therefore both very relevant to the subject, but they are not in themselves geographies.

Even when the interpretation of the title of this book has been narrowed down to these limits, there remain two main senses in

[1] J. B. Mitchell, *Historical Geography* (1954), p. 5.

which the subject could quite legitimately be discussed. Lines of communication are an essential element in economic geography. They can be seen as flows of traffic of varying volume and of varying kind. They constitute perhaps the most important single factor in the location of industry and the distribution of population. In this sense they are vital in regional geography, since all except the most backward and undeveloped territories would not be as they are if the basic communications had been different. The development of coalfields, the growth of towns, even the siting of agricultural villages are intimately dependent on the network of communications. In short they are fundamental to an interpretation of the whole landscape, and this aspect is familiar enough to anyone conversant with any geographical writing.

The other aspect is perhaps less familiar, and partly for that very reason it will be from this viewpoint that the subject will be approached in the following pages. As well as having an important influence on economic geography, communications are themselves a part of the landscape. They are elements in it, just as are hills and valleys, fields and forests, settlements and factories. Their shape, disposition, and relationship to the land-surface are not haphazard but meaningful. They are the product of numerous circumstances, and, although each part is unique, it is possible, by noting the correspondence between similar conditions where they occur in different instances, to arrive at a better understanding of the general principles which have determined the present distribution of roads, railways, canals, and other forms of communication.

Perhaps this dual approach can best be explained by an analogy. The study of a living body may fall under one of several different headings. Among these physiology and anatomy deal respectively with the study of body-processes and body structure. The two are so intimately related that neither could be properly understood without some knowledge of the other, yet they are sufficiently distinct to be accepted as separate fields of investigation for purposes of teaching, description, and research. In terms of this analogy the present work is a study of anatomy rather than of physiology. It seeks to explain the shapes, positions, and relationships of the physical parts which go to make up the whole network of communications.

There is no single yardstick by which the importance of the various elements in this network may be assessed, and, even if there were, it would be pointless to try and allot to each a ration of space proportionate to its status. Where particular kinds of communications, such as canals, exhibit features of special interest, I have not been deterred from discussing them merely on the grounds that they now play a relatively minor role in the transport geography of the country. Also I have felt justified in giving rather more emphasis to topics which have been less fully treated elsewhere. For instance, I make no apology for the fact that about half the book deals with the relationship of communications to the land-surface, since this seems to me to be one of the most important and most neglected aspects of the subject.

In choosing my examples I have been guided mainly by their suitability to illustrate the particular point at issue, but I have also attempted to spread them reasonably widely over the country. On the other hand, in all but a few cases where adequate published descriptions are available, I have confined myself to examples which I have had the opportunity of studying for myself in the field.

Although the subject-matter is drawn from Great Britain, many of the ideas discussed are more generally applicable. The physiographic limitations of this small country exclude examples of communications in high mountains such as the Alps or Andes, or in desert areas, forests, or territories of plantation economy, all of which pose their own problems. But within its own limitations Britain does contain a vast range of contrasts, and in many ways the intensive spread of communications over its more subdued relief has created an opportunity to see some of the finer and more subtle relationships which lie behind the network.

One difficulty which is inescapable concerns the use of maps. Ideally one would wish to reproduce a map for every example discussed. Since in practice this is impossible, I have tried to make the most of them by using them to illustrate examples which are particularly important or which are totally incomprehensible without them, by applying them to as wide a range of material as possible, and by making use of very different scales. In following the other examples the reader will help himself greatly if he can provide himself with good topographical maps, such as the One-inch Ordnance Survey maps, or the Quarter-inch for the study of larger areas. It will be better still if he can follow up some of them on the ground.

CHAPTER I

THE
GEOGRAPHICAL LIMITATIONS
OF COMMUNICATIONS

The theme of the first part of this book can be expressed quite simply. It is to examine the ways in which lines of communication are related to the configuration of the country across which they pass. It concerns, therefore, the fitting together of two variables—the communications and the land-surface. How far the land-surface can be described as a 'variable' will be clear to anyone who has travelled in Britain or has made a study of its physical geography, and it will later be shown how different landforms present different problems and different opportunities for the construction of communications. But first it will be necessary to examine the other variable.

It is roughly true to say that roads, railways, and canals each have their own distinctive properties and that each are related to the land-surface in characteristic ways. But the position is not as simple as this, because the precise limitations by which the construction of each kind of communication is governed, will depend in turn upon other variables. Changing techniques of construction and operation, differences in the availability of finance and in the kind of traffic to be conveyed, and many less important considerations will tend to alter the technical basis of the relationship. 'What is the steepest gradient suitable for a railway line?' is a question which just does not admit of a straight answer. Consequently one must not expect to do more than determine certain trends and certain limits which are broadly applicable to each form of transport.

The simplest case is provided by the canals. It follows from their very nature that they must consist of surfaces which are level or at least so nearly level as to make a negligible difference in an area as small as Britain. Any altitudinal changes must be achieved by some device which brings about an immediate rise from one level to another.

A small amount of vertical rise may be achieved by the use of staunches (or stanches) and flashes, which are in effect weirs with opening sections. By temporarily ponding back the water in rivers they may have the effect of raising the level enough to give an adequate draught over rapids or sections of river naturally too shallow to permit navigation. They are unsuitable on artificial cuts. They can be used only when there is no problem of water-supply and their use in modern times is extremely restricted. Edwards[1] records that examples were still (1950) to be seen in the Fens and at Pershore and Cropthorne on the Warwickshire Avon. He lists seven on the $10\frac{1}{2}$-mile stretch of the Little Ouse below Thetford, and five of these still appear on the O.S. Seventh Series map (sheet 136, Bury St. Edmunds) published in 1954, though they were not in working order at that time.

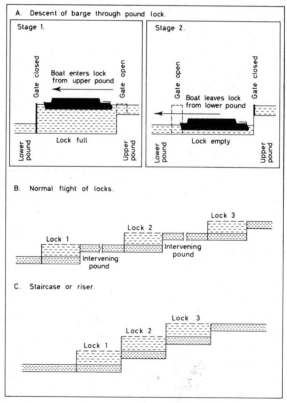

FIG. 2. DIAGRAM OF CANAL LOCKS

[1] L. A. Edwards, *Inland Waterways of Great Britain and Northern Ireland* (1950), p. 409.

By far the most common device for bringing about an alteration in level is the pound lock. It is described by Hadfield in these terms.[2]

The pound lock is that device still used on rivers and canals to alter the level of navigable water by a chamber enclosed within two sets of gates fitted with sluices. A boat enters the chamber to go downstream, the gates are shut and the water drained from the chamber through the sluices in the lower gates, till the water-level in the chamber is equal to that outside. When this is so, the lower gates are opened, and the boat moves into the lower reach. Going upwards, when the boat is to be raised, the lower gates are shut, and the lock chamber is filled with water entering through sluices in the upper gates.

From what has already been said it is clear that, strictly speaking, a canal can have no gradient, since a barge can proceed only by alternations of horizontal and vertical movement. Over any given section of canal, however, we can relate the 'rise' ($= x$) achieved in the locks to the horizontal distance ($= y$) represented by the length of the locks plus the intervening reaches or 'pounds' between the locks. By reducing x to unity and y in equal proportion we arrive at a formula of 1 in y/x, the normal form used in this country for the expression of gradients. The selection of gradients by which the line of canal is related to the land-surface obviously has a direct bearing on the choice of route, and in the present context, therefore, it becomes a matter of the greatest importance to determine (a) what rise can be practicably achieved in a lock, (b) what is the length of a lock, and (c) what distance must separate one lock from the next. This will involve some further consideration of these technical points.

There is in theory no limit to the amount of rise which can be achieved in a pound lock. In practice it is restricted by engineering difficulties and the necessity in most canals to conserve water. Very tall lock gates are more expensive to construct and maintain. In modern practice the use of the shaft lock partly overcomes the technical difficulty of building very tall gates. In the shaft lock the lower end of the lock is closed by a wall with an opening at the bottom. Only this opening has to be covered by the lock gates which may be quite small. As the water rises above the top of the gates it is contained by the wall above them. In countries where large-scale canal construction is still being undertaken, locks of this type are valuable, but they are not found on British canals.

[2] C. Hadfield, *British Canals* (1950), pp. 19–22.

With large rises there may be the additional problem of building up the banks on the reach above the lock or overdeepening the reach below. In any case they can be used only where large quantities of water are available, as on artificial sections of large navigable rivers.

No lock can operate without using water, but a boat can pass up or down an unlimited number of locks without using more than one lockful of water,[3] provided the trend (rise or fall) is uninterrupted in one direction and provided the locks occur singly, that is to say are separated from each other by intervening stretches of water. Clearly, then, the amount of water lost will depend on the volume of the largest lock. Measurements of length and breadth being generally determined by the size of the barges, it is the depth which really governs the wastage. This conflict between efficiency in traffic movement and loss of water always demands a compromise which will vary according to circumstances. Some actual examples will suggest the practical limits which apply.

The largest rise on a boat or barge canal in Britain is 14 feet in the top lock of the flight at Tardebigge (Worcester & Birmingham). McGarey says '. . . for canal locks the normal rise or lift varies between 4 and 10 feet, about seven being a usual figure for English canals. . . . The Manchester Ship Canal employs a figure of about 16 feet 6 inches. . . .'[4] The average rise on the Tardebigge flight of thirty locks is 6 feet 9 inches, on the Hatton flight of twenty-one locks it is 7 feet, on the Wigan flight, also of twenty-one locks, it is 9 feet 6 inches.

The length of a lock will be determined by the length of the boats or barges which are expected to use it. Narrow boats on British canals average about 72 feet in length. Broad barges average some 3 feet more,[5] and lock lengths are related to these measurements. The reconstructed locks on the Grand Union Canal (London–Birmingham) are 83½ feet long. Those on the Lea & Stort Navigation are long enough to take 88-foot craft.[6] Very approximately, then, the average rise of a lock is about one-tenth of its length, or, expressed in another way, a mean gradient of about 1 in 10 could be achieved if there were no intervening reaches

---

[3] More precisely the loss is equal to one lockful of water plus the volume of water displaced by the boat when ascending, and to one lockful minus the volume displaced by the boat when descending.

[4] D. G. McGarey, 'Canal locks and lifting devices in inland navigation'. *Proc. Junior Inst. Eng.* (1938), pp. 7–8.

[5] ibid., pp. 4–5.   [6] Edwards, op. cit., pp. 150–1.

between the locks. In exceptional cases locks are so arranged. They are known as 'staircase locks' and the upper gate of one lock acts as the lower gate of the next (Plate 1 and Fig. 2C). But unless a boat is following another in the same direction, its passage through a staircase requires the use of as many lockfuls of water as there are locks. In the operation of ordinary locks the pound above the lock acts as a reservoir from which it can be filled. In a staircase

Photo: John Laing & Son Ltd.

PLATE 1. WATFORD LOCKS, NORTHAMPTONSHIRE

These locks form a true staircase or 'riser' equipped with proper side-ponds, though the vegetation shows that these have been out of use for some time. Note in the background the preliminary work on the London–Yorkshire Motorway. View looking north-east.

such a reservoir is the next lock and a lower lock can only be filled by emptying the higher lock which will then have to be refilled from higher up. An added disadvantage of the staircase is that passing is not possible. Consequently one does not find large numbers of locks in staircases, the maximum being five as at Bingley on the Leeds & Liverpool Canal. The flight at Foxton (Leicestershire) contains ten locks, but there is one short but wide intermediate pound between the fifth and sixth locks, so that strictly there are two risers or staircases of five locks each.

The intervening pounds must contain a volume of water adequate to fill the lock below without a serious fall in level. The width and depth will clearly affect the issue, but McGarey suggests 300 yards as 'the minimum desirable distance between locks . . ., which therefore allows a maximum gradient of about 1 in 100, using a rise of 9 feet'.[7] By shortening the intervening pounds the gradient

Photo: Aerofilms

PLATE 2. HATTON LOCKS, WARWICKSHIRE

In this flight the locks are separated by intervening pounds. These are unusually short, but their capacity for 'feeding' the locks below is increased by widening. True side-ponds are intermediate in elevation between the water-surfaces of the lock when full and empty, whereas the widenings shown here are not. They enable the pounds between the locks to be shorter and the mean gradient of the flight to be correspondingly increased, but they do not save water. View looking north-north-west.

could be considerably steepened. To turn again to an example, the gradient of the Tardebigge flight is about 1 in 50. That of the Hatton flight is even steeper, thanks to the shortness of the intervening pounds (Plate 2).

In spite of the availability of various devices such as the use of

[7] McGarey, op. cit., p. 10.

duplicate locks, side-ponds, etc., to aid its conservation, a shortage of water is often a major consideration in planning the route. While it is true that, except in a staircase lock, a boat will use only one lockful of water in negotiating a flight of locks, this applies only to a section of canal where the locks are all rising (or falling) in the same direction. Every time the trend alters (rising locks being succeeded by falling locks, or vice-versa) a new sequence is established and a further lockful of water will be needed when a boat passes. For instance, let AB and CD be two canals of equal length, each having ten locks separated by intervening pounds. In AB these are so arranged that five rising locks are succeeded by five falling locks. A barge passing from A to B will use one lockful of water in reaching the summit and another lockful in descending from the summit. In the canal CD, however, the locks are arranged alternately, each rising lock being succeeded by a falling lock. A barge passing from C to D will then use ten lockfuls as against two lockfuls in the canal AB. The geographical implication of this is of the greatest importance, for it means that, where an engineer is obliged to carry a line over a physical obstacle and down the other side, he must as far as possible eliminate all secondary summits, rising progressively to a single summit pound (furnished with adequate water-supply), and falling progressively beyond it. As we shall see later the available land-surface does not always behave in so simple a fashion, and for this reason the canals present in some ways the most interesting problems of adaptation to physiography.

It was partly the limitations of gradient and partly the wastage of water, inevitable with the use of the pound lock, which caused engineers to have recourse to other methods of changing elevation on canals. These included inclined planes, inclined lifts, and vertical lifts. Hadfield mentions inclined planes on the Bude, Tavistock, Torrington, Chard, Grand Western, Somersetshire Coal, Shrewsbury, Shropshire, Grand Junction, and Monkland Canals and makes more detailed reference to the planes at the Ketley ironworks (Shropshire) and at Foxton (Leicestershire).[8] Among the canal lifts he mentions are seven on the Grand Western Canal's Taunton extension, one on the Somersetshire Coal Canal and one on the Worcester and Birmingham at Tardebigge (Worcestershire) in addition to the one surviving example at Anderton, near Northwich (Plate 3). The rises of these devices

[8] Hadfield, op. cit., pp. 59–60 and 219.

varied considerably. The Tardebigge lift was of 12 feet; those on the Grand Western Canal of 16 to 46 feet and the Anderton 50 feet 4 inches. The inclined plane at Ketley had a rise of 73 feet according to Telford, and the Foxton plane 75 feet. This last was constructed on a gradient of about 1 in 4 and was steeper than

Photo: S. H. Beaver

PLATE 3. THE ANDERTON BOAT LIFT, NORTHWICH, CHESHIRE

The Anderton Boat Lift was built in 1874 (it has been considerably modified since) to make a connexion between the Trent & Mersey Canal and the River Weaver (right), thereby providing a more direct route between the Potteries and the lower part of the Mersey estuary. View to the south-east.

most. The inclined plane[9] on the Monkland Canal, for instance, had a gradient of 1 in 10.[10]

It will be noted that many of the examples quoted occur in the West Country, and this is due to the preference for mechanical lifts shown by the engineer Green who carried out a great deal of

---

[9] Hadfield describes all these devices as 'inclined planes'. McGarey restricts the term to those planes where boats are carried directly on wheels or wheeled carriages. On the Monkland Canal and at Foxton the boats were carried in water-tanks which were hauled up the incline. These McGarey calls 'inclined lifts'.

[10] McGarey, op. cit., p. 13.

work there and 'solved in terms of his medium the problem presented by the hilly country of the south-west of England'.[11]

It can be seen, then, that the devices employed for bringing about changes in altitude varied considerably in their methods of operation and in the amount of 'lift' which they could provide. They had, however, the common property of achieving their lifts vertically, apart from the inclined planes, and here the horizontal displacement was extremely limited. The Foxton plane, for instance, had a length of only 100 yards. Whether locks, lifts, or inclined planes were employed, the basic principle remained the same—long stretches of level surface punctuated by sudden steps.

This 'rigidity', which, as far as elevation is concerned, is a feature of all canals, contrasts sharply with the freedom they enjoy in manœuvring in a horizontal plane. The curves which can be employed are limited only by the size of the vessels which have to negotiate them. Although extremely acute changes in direction may necessitate some reduction in speeds, these are in any case so low that the resulting disadvantage is not very great. There are practically no limits to the angles through which canals can turn if need be, and a moment's reflection will show that this is their saving grace, because it means that, even if the contour lines twist and turn, the canals are able to follow them and so maintain their uniform elevation without constant interruption.

These technical requirements remained more or less constant throughout the whole period during which canals were constructed, and it will therefore be found that the selection of routes by canal engineers has always been influenced by similar considerations. Where the surface was sufficiently undulating to have any effect on the route chosen, the contour lines were the major guide to the engineer. It is true that later engineers, notably Telford, tended to favour straighter routes, and that this practice involved more frequent departures from the natural contours and a greater reliance on embankments and cuttings, such as the cutting near Norbury (Staffordshire) and the Landsdowne Cutting, near Solihull (Warwickshire), but it merely had the effect of rendering the canal more independent of the land-surface; it did not involve any departure from the principle of the alternation of long horizontal and short vertical movements.

The relation between railways and the land-surface is governed

[11] C. Hadfield, 'James Green as canal engineer'. *Jnl. of Transport History*, vol. 1 (1953), p. 44.

by quite different requirements, which did not, as in the case of canals, remain comparatively constant. Ideally a railway should be perfectly level and perfectly straight, but it is only rarely that the configuration of the ground makes this possible for more than a short distance. Any departure from this ideal implies some loss of efficiency. It is true that some independence of the land-surface can be obtained by the use of tunnels, cuttings, embankments, viaducts, and so on, but these are expensive devices, and the more they are used to maintain level gradients and gentle curves the greater will be the cost of construction. In practice, therefore, a compromise has to be reached, the nature of which will be determined by the particular circumstances of every case, and it is only within broad limits that one can generalize about current practice at any given period.

At the beginning of the nineteenth century most of the railways in operation were used for the conveyance of minerals, particularly coal, and since they were mostly designed to move coal from the coalfields to navigable water it was frequently possible to make use of gravitation in moving the wagons. And further, by using rope-haulage, the loaded wagons moving downhill could be made to pull the empties up. But where it was necessary to move appreciable quantities of traffic in both directions this principle was of limited application and other methods had to be used.

Up to about 1830 many engineers preferred to divide their track into two distinct categories. A level section was maintained as long as possible, over which the wagons were pulled by horses or locomotives, then, to make height suddenly, a rope-incline was used, operated by a stationary steam-engine. The system can be seen at once to be analogous to that of the canals, where locks and flights of locks alternated with long level sections. Many such rope-inclines were built after 1830, but in general the rope-inclines became superseded by longer and more gentle gradients. The Leeds & Selby Railway may be taken to illustrate this point. A line between Leeds and Selby was surveyed in 1825 by George Stephenson as part of the Leeds & Hull company's route. To the east of Leeds the cuesta of the Magnesian Limestone interposed a barrier which had to be crossed between Garforth and Micklefield at an altitude of over 250 feet. Stephenson decided that this could be surmounted only by rope-inclines and provided for these in his survey. Mainly for financial reasons the scheme could not be carried out at this date and it was not until 1830 that the railway was authorized from Leeds as far as Selby. Meanwhile the directors had engaged another engineer, James Walker, to re-survey the line, and it was to his plans that it was built.

Walker introduced several modifications in Stephenson's plans among which was the recommendation that the rope-inclines should be dispensed with and replaced by more gentle gradients.[12] Accordingly a line was built suitable for working by locomotives, which included a gradient of 3¾ miles at 1 in 136 on the eastward descent near South Milford (Fig. 3A). This was in operation by 1834.

The more conservative engineers, including George Stephenson, were still reluctant to use gradients as steep as this for locomotive working, and opinion as to what was a reasonable gradient for a main line was extremely diverse at this date, as the following instance will illustrate. During 1835 surveys were made for a line from Derby to Leeds which resulted in the incorporation of the North Midland Railway (1836). The easiest route lay along the Rother valley between Chesterfield and Rotherham, but this had the disadvantage of passing to the east of Sheffield which lay further up the Don valley. It was generally agreed that it would have been desirable to carry the line through Sheffield if this could have been done without the use of unreasonable gradients. We know from subsequent events that, with the aid of a tunnel 2,027 yards long (at Bradway), it was possible to build such a line (it was opened in 1870), using a maximum gradient of 1 in 100. But this was far too steep for Stephenson, who regarded 1 in 330 as the maximum practicable gradient for a main line, and the Rother Valley line was duly built[13] (Fig. 3B & C).

In view of this it is interesting to see what was the practice of Stephenson's contemporaries in choosing maximum gradients for their lines. In 1837 the Sheffield–Manchester line via Penistone was authorized and this involved a stretch of over two miles near Hadfield at 1 in 100 and a continuous stretch of 1 in 117 for five miles up to the west portal of the Woodhead Tunnel. Or again, in the Parliamentary Session of 1836 the Eastern Counties Railway was authorized, and its mainline involved a climb of over two miles to Brentwood (Essex) at 1 in 103. The Great Western (1835) had included a stretch of nearly two miles at 1 in 100 through the Box Tunnel (Fig. 3E). Most remarkable of all was the Lickey Incline

---

[12] J. Walker, *Report on the Leeds & Selby Railway* (1829).
[13] See, for instance, F. S. Williams, *The Midland Railway* (1877).

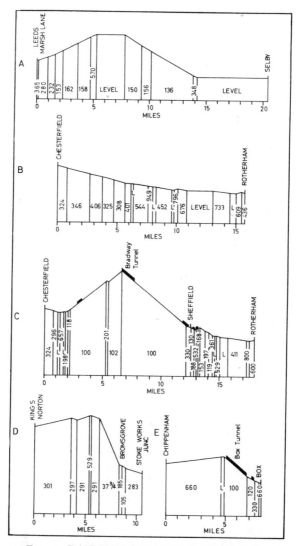

FIG. 3. RAILWAY GRADIENT PROFILES

A. Leeds–Selby. Former N.E.R.
B. Chesterfield–Rotherham direct (Rother Valley line). Former Midland Rly.
C. Chesterfield–Rotherham via Sheffield. Former Midland Rly.
D. The Lickey Incline (Birmingham–Gloucester line, King's Norton to Stoke Works Junc.). Former Midland Rly.
E. Chippenham–Box. Former G.W.R. (Paddington–Bristol).

Source: 'Gradients of the British Main Line Railways'

on the Birmingham & Gloucester Railway (1836) about two miles in length at no less a gradient than 1 in 37¾. Stephenson was not alone in forecasting that the Lickey Incline could not be worked by locomotives, his opinion being shared by Brunel, the engineer of the Box Tunnel, but they were both proved wrong. At this date, then, there was a difference of nearly nine times between the maximum gradients advocated by Stephenson for the North Midland and by Moorsom for the Birmingham & Gloucester (Fig. 3D).

After the eighteen-thirties such wide variation in professional opinion is no longer discernible, neither is the progressive trend towards the general use of steeper gradients. Although the severity of gradients in common use continued to vary between one company and another and more particularly between one type of country and another, no significant contrasts emerge from a comparison between gradients adopted at different periods. If, for instance, one compares the gradients used on the King's Cross–Doncaster line with those of the Great Central line between Quainton Road (near Aylesbury) and Nottingham—lines constructed for similar kinds of traffic and through similar types of country—it can be seen that the ruling gradients are also similar; yet nearly half a century separates the two lines. Or again, an example from more hilly country shows that the gradients of Beattock Bank (about 1 in 75) are a little steeper than the heaviest gradients of the Totley–Chinley (Sheffield–Manchester) line (1 in 100), which was built forty-five years later through country scarcely, if any, less difficult.

Some of the steepest gradients in use in Britain were not designed with a view to their being worked by locomotive traction at all. The old rope-inclines, operated by stationary steam-engines, have long been superseded, except in a few instances chiefly on mineral lines.[14] Sometimes the change-over involved the provision of a new section of line better suited to locomotives. Thus the rope-incline which carried the original Stockton & Darlington Railway over the Magnesian Limestone escarpment was replaced by the Shildon Tunnel, and the coal trains could then be worked all the way from Weardale to the coast by locomotive. On the Whitby & Pickering Railway (authorized in 1833) the Goathland Incline was replaced by a better-graded section following more closely the

---

[14] For example on the Cromford & High Peak line and in the North-west Durham Coalfield.

valley of the Eller Beck.[15] But in many cases there was no such replacement, and locomotives are today hauling trains regularly over sections of line built to be worked by rope-haulage. The inclines from Euston to Camden, Lime Street (Liverpool) to Edge Hill, and Queen Street (Glasgow) to Cowlairs are examples, though the gradients of the first two, with maxima at 1 in 70 and 1 in 83 respectively, are less steep than many lines intended for locomotive working. The Cowlairs Incline is mainly at 1 in 41. The branch line from Middleton Junction to Oldham (Werneth), which was originally worked by rope-haulage, has a gradient of 1 in 27. Normington[16] describes how, in an emergency, an attempt had to be made to take a train up it by locomotive-power, and this being eventually successful, the rope-haulage was abandoned.

On the South Devon (former G.W.R.) line between Exeter and Plymouth the very heavy gradients are at least partly related to the system of traction by which it was intended to work the line at the time when the gradients were determined. The general course of the line authorized under the South Devon Railway Act of 1844 was substantially the same as that of the present line but the maximum gradients were less severe. Shortly after the passage of the Act the directors, on the advice of their engineer, Brunel, decided to install the so-called Atmospheric System of traction, patented some five years earlier by Messrs Clegg and Samuda, which consisted of a continuous 15-inch pipe from which the air was pumped by stationary steam-engines situated at intervals of three miles or thereabouts, and through which a piston was drawn, impelled by atmospheric pressure, the piston being connected to the trains through a longitudinal valve in the pipe which opened and closed as the piston passed.[17] Although the apparatus was only brought into operation between Exeter and Newton Abbot, it was the anticipation of using this form of traction on the inclines west of that point which induced Brunel to modify the authorized route by steepening the gradients. This was one of the ways in which he proposed to offset the cost of the atmospheric equipment, and he argued that its use would enable the trains to be worked satisfactorily over gradients which he would not have been justified in adopting for locomotives. The inclines

---

[15] W. W. Tomlinson; *The North Eastern Railway* (1914), p. 484.
[16] Thomas Normington, *The Lancashire & Yorkshire Railway* (1898).
[17] E. T. MacDermot, *History of the Great Western Railway*, vol. II, q.v. for a detailed description of the apparatus (p. 199 et seq.).

at Dainton, Rattery, and Hemerdon,[18] difficult as they would have been if constructed to the original plans, were made even worse on the supposition that they were to be worked by a method which in the event was never used.

It can now be understood why there can be no simple answer to the question, 'How steep a gradient can an engineer use in surveying his line?' One can merely cite examples of gradients which have actually been used. Details of these gradients can be found in the Parliamentary Plans and Sections deposited with the Bills authorizing the construction of the railways concerned. Those for most of the main lines of British railways have been published.[19] For a recent view of the maximum gradients suitable for railways one may refer to the figures given by R. V. Hughes[20] namely, for main lines 1 in 100, with a reduction to 1 in 260 through stations; for suburban lines 1 in 60 if worked by steam; if all-electric they can be at 1 in 40 or even steeper. Hughes is at pains to explain that these are only approximate limits and that they have often been exceeded in practice. In any case the use of gradients as steep as this has a serious effect on running speeds. Again figures by the same author may be quoted. A modern steam locomotive, he says, pulling 15 bogie-vehicles of passenger stock, estimated at 450 tons tare, might be expected to maintain speeds of 50–60 m.p.h. up a gradient of 1 in 200 under average weather conditions, whereas the comparable figure at 1 in 100 would be only 30–35 m.p.h.

Although it is theoretically possible to counteract the centrifugal force of a train moving on a curve, there are several reasons why sharp curves are unsuitable, and it is the relative validity of these reasons which determines how sharp it is permissible to make the curves in any given instance. Among these reasons may be mentioned the following. (1) The greater the curve the greater the limit imposed on the wheelbase of vehicles, particularly locomotives. (2) The outer wheel of a vehicle travelling on a curve has farther to go than the inner wheel, but since on most vehicles the wheels are fixed to the axles, it follows that there can be no differential between the number of revolutions made by the outer and inner wheels, and that the difference in distance travelled by each must therefore be at least partly accounted for by slipping on the

---

[18] The maximum gradients are as follows: Dainton 1 in 36, Rattery 1 in 46, and Hemerdon 1 in 41.

[19] *Gradients of the British Main Line Railways*. The Railway Publishing Co., London (1938).

[20] R. V. Hughes in *Town and Country Planning Textbook* (1950), p. 338 et seq.

rails.[21] This results in a great increase in friction. (3) The method of counteracting the centrifugal force is by canting, that is raising the outer rail above the level of the inner. This can be done to balance the outward thrust, provided the speed of the train is known. But obviously uniformity of train speed over a given section of track can never be assumed, and the degree of canting required to compensate the outward thrust of an express train moving at 80 miles an hour cannot be correct for a goods train travelling at 20 or for the same express train should it be stopped by signals on that length of track. (4) The outward thrust of a train on a canted curve is transmitted to the track, which on a sharp curve is therefore more likely to be displaced out of its proper alignment. (5) In certain circumstances adequate canting cannot be used. For instance at junctions it is not possible to provide the ideal cant for each diverging track, and it may be that the more the cant is adjusted to one track the less appropriate will it be to the other. Modern engineering techniques have greatly advanced, and at some junctions it has been possible to dispense with severe speed restrictions on both tracks, but at others the policy is to provide a cant appropriate to the main line, and in this case severe speed restrictions are essential for trains on the branch line.

As with the gradients so with curves it is possible to distinguish between practices adopted in the early period of railway building and those of later date. The main lines of the eighteen-thirties, for instance, can often be identified on Ordnance Survey one-inch maps by the gentleness of their curves compared with those of later lines, but here again after the eighteen thirties no consistent or progressive changes in practice are apparent.

With regard to curves Hughes[22] suggests that for a gauge of 4 feet 8½ inches a cant of 6 inches may be regarded as the maximum practicable, and this would automatically impose limits to the radius of curves designed to carry traffic at known maximum speeds. Thus a 6-inch cant would be sufficient for a train travelling at 60 m.p.h. on a curve of 35½ chains radius, but the equivalent radius for 100 m.p.h. would be 98 chains. Hughes cites the following figures for curves commonly employed:

In points and crossings:

For trains arriving at stations and due to stop	21½ chs.
For trains starting from stations	14½ chs.
For shunting movements	10 chs.

[21] Part of the difference may be accounted for by the 'coning' of wheel tyres.
[22] Hughes, op. cit.

In sidings:

Where train engines are to be used	8 chs.
For short-wheelbase shunting locos	4 chs.
For capstan working	3 chs.

If it is true of railways that their limitations vary with the requirements of different kinds of traffic, it is even more true of roads, which can be said to include everything downwards from arterial roads for fast traffic to service and access roads, even trackways and bridle-ways—almost anything, in fact, according to where one wishes to draw the limits of definition. Where the circumstances demand, roads exhibit a much greater flexibility than canals or railways. They rival the canals in their ability to negotiate sharp angles; they surpass the railways in their ability to surmount inclines, being generally able to maintain gradients several times as steep, always at the sacrifice of some efficiency in the matter of speed and sometimes of safety.

Unlike the canals and railways the roads have seen in the immediate past, say the last four decades, increases in the speed of traffic which have made entirely new demands from the technical point of view, and which have revolutionized the principles which had earlier governed the relationship between road and land-surface. The result has been that the road-pattern of Britain until well into the present century consisted entirely of various parts none of which had been constructed to carry traffic at more than about 15 miles an hour. Clearly, therefore, the physical behaviour of vehicles travelling at speeds in excess of this had no influence on the determination of the lines of route before that time. The new standards have made totally new demands, and these have been reflected in a complex process of adaptation and supplementation which are gradually making their mark on the system wherever the old order failed to measure up to the new requirements. Thus it is even more impossible to give a figure for the maximum per-missible gradient of a road than of a railway. In extreme cases motor roads may reach gradients as steep as 1 in 3. Regular bus services are certainly operated on gradients of 1 in $4\frac{1}{2}$. But these cannot be regarded as satisfactory for modern traffic. They have been made by putting modern surfaces on old trackways and calling them motor roads. Many such gradients are to be found on by-roads where the volume of traffic coupled with the difficulty of the terrain would not warrant the realignment of the road, but some of the steepest, such as Porlock (Somerset), Little Gruinard

(Ross-shire), Kirkstone (Westmorland), all with maxima at 1 in 4, or Holne Chase and Countisbury, both in Devon, with maxima at 1 in $3\frac{1}{2}$, are to be found on A-class roads.

Gradients of this severity, however, can only be regarded as freaks in roads of this class. A hundred years before the advent of the motor road Telford laid down 'that no main road should be steeper than 1 in 30, which figure is also favoured by the Ministry of Transport at the present time'[23] (1950). As in railway construction, so in road surveying engineers varied in their assessments of what was best. One of Telford's reports, for instance, contains this sentence: 'Having also observed, that many roads are rendered imperfect by having the steepest ascent towards the end of a stage, I have, in laying out this direct line, reversed that order.'[24] In the same Report he recognizes that steep gradients alternating with more level sections may be less injurious to horses than long inclined planes. These views would hardly be likely to influence modern trunk road construction, but many miles of our present main roads follow the lines laid down by the man who expressed them (see Chapter VI).

The Ministry of Transport Memorandum of 1947[25] may be taken as a general guide to the standards of design which have influenced road construction since the war, though at the time of writing this is about to be superseded. Where the ruling gradient of 1 in 30 could not be maintained, 1 in 20 was recommended as a desirable limit. The limit suggested for the radius of curves on main roads was given as 300 feet, but 1,000 feet was regarded as a figure to be used wherever possible. Road widths are closely related to capacity and this will be referred to later (Chapter V), while those technical properties of other kinds of communication which have a bearing on their geography are further discussed in Chapter VIII.

The properties and requirements of these various kinds of communications, therefore, have limited their geographical occurrence, particularly altitudinally. The highest level reached by any canal was 638 feet on the Huddersfield Narrow Canal at Standedge[26] (Plate 24). This is exceeded by railways at many summits,

[23] R. B. Hounsfield in *Town and Country Planning Textbook* (1950), p. 330.
[24] T. Telford, 'Report respecting the road from Carlisle to Glasgow' (Appx. to *Report of the Select Committee on the Carlisle & Glasgow road*) (1815), p. 15.
[25] Ministry of Transport, *Memorandum on the Layout and Construction of Roads*, No. 575 (1947).
[26] Edwards, op. cit., p. 134.

the highest being Drumochter (1,484 feet) on the main line through the Grampians between Perth and Inverness.[27] Roads reach higher altitudes still. At Cairnwell the Spittal of Glenshee to Braemar road (A.93) is at 2,200 feet. The eighteenth-century road over the Pass of Corrie Yairack went even higher (2,507 feet), but this never survived long enough to become a motor road.

It is not, however, in any absolute limits of this sort that one will find the most eloquent expression of these differences. They are reflected in the whole delicately balanced relat⁁nship between the lines of communication on the one hand and the manifold forms and features of the land-surface on the other.

[27] The Snowdon rack-railway reaches more than twice this height.

CHAPTER II

VALLEYS AS ROUTEWAYS

It is sometimes said that railways are confined to valleys, while roads are comparatively independent of them. This contains a large grain of truth, but it requires so many qualifications that it can be accepted only as a very broad generalization. It derives from the assumption that valleys afford the desiderata which, as has been shown, are more important in the construction of railways than roads, namely the opportunity for using gentle gradients and gentle curves. They may do so, but they may not. The relationship between lines of communication and the land-surface is something far more complicated than the mere utilization of valleys. Furthermore, valleys are of many different kinds, and their suitability for carrying roads, railways, and canals is at least in part related to their mode of occurrence. Some of the more distinctive types of valley will presently be considered and their suitability for these purposes discussed, but first there are a few points of more general significance.

A so-called 'Natural Routeway' is a means and not an end. It affords the opportunity for communication; it does not create the demand. Nevertheless, since the distribution of settlements, particularly urban settlements, has tended to be closely linked with communications, there is a sense in which the existence of natural routeways has contributed to the demand for their use. Most of the towns in Britain trace their origin back to the times when the rivers were themselves the principal means of transport at least for bulky materials, and this put a premium on the banks of navigable waterways as potential town sites. There were many other reasons for the siting of towns in valleys, such as the availability of water-supply and in some cases of water-power, the convergence of land-routes on bridges, particularly if the river concerned were too wide to be bridged except at infrequent intervals, and the fact that the valleys often, though not always, afforded the best agricultural land, so that the towns, as market-centres, grew up on valley-sites. Many of these factors have changed greatly in value since the original location of the towns, but the tendency, with certain striking exceptions, has been to build on to the existing towns, provided they afford the requirements of modern industrial development, and in this way most of our modern towns have come to occupy positions dictated by the needs of earlier days.

If, then, the objective of most communications has been to connect towns, and if most towns are sited in valleys, it may be supposed that most lines will be concerned with connecting one valley-site with another, and this is broadly true especially of railways and canals. And if all towns were interconnected by valley-systems, no doubt nearly all the railways of the country and many of the roads too, would occupy valleys. Certainly where towns are linked by suitable valleys it is the normal practice for them to be linked by valley-railways.

It must be remembered that it is not the valley *per se* that the engineer is looking for, but a strip of land as level and as straight as possible between his termini, and many valleys are conspicuously unable to provide this. It may well be that older erosion-surfaces at higher levels exhibit these requirements more fully, and examples of such cases will be considered in the next chapter. But since there is a prima facie case for supposing that many lines of communication do follow valleys, it is reasonable to begin with an examination of the main physical features of valleys with a view to determining how far they are able to afford the facilities demanded by different forms of communication as discussed in Chapter I.

Water-eroded valleys in an early stage of development are not usually well suited to the building of communications. Nearly all their characteristic properties are such as to make difficult the construction of roads and even more so of canals and railways. In valleys of this kind the stream is still downcutting actively. This means first that the long-profile of the valley is steep, at least in parts, and may well contain waterfalls, so that a level surface along the valley-bottom is not to be expected. Secondly, considering the cross-profile of the young valley, active downcutting means that the stream is likely to fill the whole valley floor, there being no flood-plain or well-developed terraces to provide a suitable path; neither are the valley-sides, which have an important part to play in the geography of communications, able to help here. Owing to the dominant role of downcutting (vertical corrasion) they are invariably steep, and it frequently happens that projections of bare rock or a thin cover of unstable debris, add to the complications. Thirdly, when we consider a young valley in plan, its efficiency as a routeway may prove to be greatly impaired by the occurrence of overlapping or 'interlocking' spurs. A horizontal line drawn along the valley-side (that is to say a contour line) will then be extremely sinuous, and a road or railway following it must describe equal convolutions or become separated from the surface, which, it has been shown, can only be achieved with additional expense.

Before considering actual examples of young valleys used by communications it will be as well to see how they contrast with water-eroded valleys in a more mature stage of development.

As the evolution of the river-valley progresses, the main obstacles characteristic of a young valley disappear. The longitudinal profile is smoothed out and the steps in the valley-floor, which are a normal feature of youth, are eliminated. As the stream cuts sideways the valley-floor is widened and the valley-sides recede. This is particularly important in the case of railways, owing to their inability to negotiate sharp curves. Even though the valley may remain sinuous, the increased width of the valley-floor means that the precise course of a railway is much less rigidly dictated and that it has much more room to manœuvre within the valley-bottom, so that, by passing if necessary from one side to the other, it can negotiate the twists of the valley using moderate curves which would have been quite impossible in the youthful stage. Furthermore, as the process of downcutting is now retarded, the valley-slopes will tend to become less steep and the upland surfaces separating one valley from another will be attacked, with the result that, if it should be necessary to take the line out of the valley, the task is now much easier. The more gently sloping sides may also be useful in providing a path for a railway along the side of the valley and above the flood-plain.

After the initial development of a flood-plain further deepening may take place and a new flood-plain be formed at a lower level. In this case it often happens that vestiges of the earlier flood-plain or plains will remain as river-terraces, and since these are almost level surfaces, rising at very gentle gradients upstream, they afford still further scope to the engineer.

In a typical mature valley, then, one can distinguish three likely types of minor landform suitable for carrying lines of communication: (i) the 'solid' rock of the valley-sides, (ii) the river-terraces, and (iii) the alluvium of the present flood-plain. The relative suitability of each will probably be governed by local circumstances, but there are certain limitations which frequently seem to apply. Thus the valley-side site offers less scope for flexibility, particularly if it is steep; and, if the line of route rises appreciably above the valley-bottom, difficulty may be encountered in crossing tributary valleys. Terraces, on the other hand, while offering a greater breadth for manœuvre at a constant level, are liable to interruption, particularly at the junction of tributary valleys or where they have been cut away by the stream. Finally the flood-plain may provide a less firm bed for the road or track and its liability to flood may even necessitate the building of a causeway or embankment.

If we follow Davis's cycle concept[1] into its final stage of old age we find that the further modifications of the valley-form are of less importance for our purpose. They are changes of degree, accentuating still further the emancipation from the stringent limitations of youth, particularly in the lowering of the divides separating one valley from another. The real contrast lies between those valleys which have reached maturity and those which have not, and to the latter we must add valley-sections which have been subject to rejuvenation.

When a fall takes place in the base-level of a river, it will result in a vigorous resumption of downcutting and the ultimate re-grading of the river to the new base-level. A river in this condition is said to be rejuvenated, and there are in Britain many valleys, the upper portions of which exhibit all the features of maturity while the lower portions are deeply entrenched in freshly cut channels below the former valley-floor. Where this happens there is a striking difference between each section of the valley as a potential routeway, the upper or mature section offering few difficulties, while the lower portion imposes all the obstacles associated with a youthful valley.

For a fuller description of the physical properties of various types of valley reference should be made to a textbook of geomorphology, but the few details which have been given here should be adequate to illustrate the very different opportunities which each type affords, and some actual examples can now be considered.

From what has been said about youthful valleys it will be clear

[1] W. M. Davis, 'The Geographical Cycle'. *G.J.* xiv (1899), p. 481.

that their negative aspect is the most striking. Numerous such valleys have been developed on the glaciated surfaces of the coastal areas of County Durham (where they are known as 'denes') and north-east Yorkshire. It follows that these valleys are post-glacial in age, and the time which has elapsed since the retreat of the ice has been insufficient to allow erosion to proceed beyond an early stage. A glance at the Ordnance Survey one-inch maps (sheets 85 and 86) will show these valleys as linear strips of woodland leading down to the sea. Very occasionally one finds a minor road following them for a short distance. But with very few exceptions indeed these post-glacial ravines are entirely devoid of communications of any kind. This is not due to the fact that they run in the wrong direction. In north-east Yorkshire, for instance, they are paralleled by several minor roads leading inland from the sea, but these invariably keep to the higher land.

On the North Devon coast a similar pattern occurs. Here the upland (Lynton) surface is crossed by several streams which have been described in the following terms:

> There is a striking contrast between the valleys of the lower and middle reaches of the rivers within the area of the Lynton surface. The difference arises from a recent strong rejuvenation which has extended only a limited distance upstream. Thus the lower reaches have valleys which are typically juvenile while the middle reaches are more mature. The valley-form of the lower reaches is a V-shaped gorge, so narrow at the bottom that there is no room for a road beside the river. . . .[2]

Where roads do follow these valleys, as between Lynmouth and Watersmeet, they become famous for their scenic value, but the majority keep to the high ground. The A.39 road, for instance, between Lynmouth and Porlock, passes high above the Lyn River and the wooded ravine of Hawk Combe. In a very different geographical context the chines of Bournemouth might be cited to illustrate the same point.

Railways, as might be expected, have even more difficulty in accommodating themselves to the conditions presented by youthful valleys. In Britain they use them only for short distances and under particular circumstances, for instance in obtaining access from a lowland to a plateau where the plateau-edge presents a wall-like obstacle into which young valleys have cut notches (Plate 4). Unsuitable as such valleys may be, they mitigate the

---

[2] Scott Simpson, 'The development of the Lyn drainage system and its relation to the origin of the coast between Combe Martin and Porlock'. *P.G.A.* 64 (1953), p. 14.

Photo: Aerofilms, by permission of Holywell Textile Mills Ltd.

PLATE 4. THE HOLYWELL BRANCH, FLINTSHIRE

The town of Holywell (top right) is built on a shelf-like surface on the Carboni-ferous Limestone. This surface is being attacked by a small stream which flows north-eastwards (left) to the Dee estuary at Greenfield. The profile of its valley, and of the tiny tributary in the foreground, is one of 'youth'. Although it leaves much to be desired as a path for the railway, it provides the only practicable means by which the line could fall 300 feet from its terminus (beyond the railway bridge, top right) to the coastline at Holywell Junction in about a mile and a half. The ruling gradient is 1 in 27. View towards the south-south-east.

otherwise very difficult task of surmounting the obstacle. Glen Farg in Perthshire will serve as an example. As with so many of the valleys of central Scotland it is strictly a rejuvenated valley, the upper portions exhibiting more mature features, but where it crosses the Ochil Hills it has all the features of a youthful profile.

The Edinburgh–Perth line of the former North British Railway, having crossed the Forth Bridge, runs by Dunfermline and Cow-denbeath to the small plateau in which is situated Loch Leven. The surface of the Loch is at 351 feet above sea-level and most of the plateau is a little higher. To the north-west the plateau is bounded by the Ochil Hills, and, although to the north of Kinross these are moderate in height, a continuous escarpment stretches east-north-east overlooking the mouth of the Earn and the Firth of Tay. The northern face of this escarpment is drained by a number of streams, of which that flowing through Glen Farg affords the easiest passage. This stream falls over 400 feet from Glenfarg village to the flood-plain of the River Earn in about four miles. The railway also has to fall rapidly to reach the Earn flood-plain at Bridge of Earn, and in doing so is able to use the glen. Although the line is falling at 1 in 75 the river has cut down its bed much more steeply, and to maintain a gradient even of 1 in 75 the railway is forced to abandon the glen and swing west-wards, completing its descent by an oblique course down the face of the escarpment. To accomplish this the engineering works are heavy and include two tunnels, the upper one to carry the line through a projecting spur, the lower one to pierce the western valley-side at the point where the line leaves the glen. The valley is followed for little more than three miles, but in that distance about half of the descent from the summit to the plain has been accomplished.

The wall-like northern face of the Millstone Grit where it overlooks Wharfedale in the Chevin is strongly reminiscent of the Ochils escarpment though rather less high. Here also a railway, in this case the main line from Leeds to Harrogate, has to pass through the obstacle more or less at right angles. But in this case there is no youthful valley notching the face of the obstacle and the railway cannot find a passage comparable with that of Glen Farg. The alternative solution has been to build a tunnel (Bram-hope) over two miles long underneath the summit of the obstacle, emerging about half-way up the scarp face near Arthington Station. In the case of Glen Farg the youthful valley, even though it does not offer the ideal route, has made the crossing of the higher barrier the lesser task of the two.

The area around the Severn Gorge (Shropshire) affords some good examples of railways following rejuvenated valleys. Since the gorge was formed as a result of the glacial diversion of the Severn it follows that the downcutting of such a deep valley in such a short time has involved a rapid lowering of the base-levels of the tributary streams which join it in this reach, and all of them exhibit youthful features. On the plateau to the north of the Gorge and to the east of the Wrekin the Coal Measures come to the surface to form a small but at one time quite important coalfield. Based partly on the coal but partly on other locational factors, there grew up here a concentration of iron and other industries. The gorge contains rapids, and the head of navigation lay at its south-eastern end near Coalport. It therefore became essential to connect this plateau with the river below this point, and this was done first by a canal with an associated inclined plane and later by a railway which crosses the plateau from Oakengates and at Madeley enters the valley of a small tributary which falls rapidly to the Severn. It is a youthful valley, steep-sided and by no means ideal for railway construction, but it serves to provide a route for the railway which uses it to begin its descent before completing it diagonally down the slope of the main (Severn) valley-side to Coalport.

Some two miles farther to the west the Lydebrook follows a very similar course. When in 1862 the Severn Valley Line was opened through the Severn Gorge, thereby providing a route southwards towards Worcester and westwards towards Shrewsbury, the desirability of connecting up this through railway with the Dawley–Oakengates plateau became obvious, and the Lydebrook valley offered a steep but not impossible route through Coalbrookdale. On the southern side of the river the Severn Valley Railway threw out a branch to the little town of Much Wenlock (later extended to Craven Arms) which lies more than 300 feet above the level of the main line at Buildwas Junction. Here a small stream, rising in the broad vale of the Lower Ludlow Shales near Much Wenlock, has cut a gorge through the Wenlock Limestone in Farley Dingle, and by following its steep and twisty descent the railway can find a reasonable path to the banks of the Severn.

On the East Coast main line between London and Edinburgh easily the most severe gradient is the descent from the mature valley of the Eye Water near Grantshouse to the coastal lowland at Cockburnspath. (There is a slightly steeper but much shorter gradient in the immediate approach to Waverley Station, Edinburgh.) The upper half of the descent to Cockburnspath, which stretches for $4\frac{1}{2}$ miles at 1 in 96, lies in the valley of a small, immature stream, though, as in Glen Farg, the line has to leave the valley, which is too steep for it, and complete its descent in more open country.

Perhaps the best example of the use of immature valleys to connect a plateau with an adjacent lowland is to be found in the Forest of Dean. Structurally it consists of a basin rimmed by outward-facing escarpments of Old Red Sandstone and Carboniferous rocks. The small collieries working coal in the basin gave rise to the building of several railways, some of pre-locomotive date, later reconstructed for locomotive working, and these railways comprised a small network in the Forest with outlets to the railways of the surrounding lowlands at five points. On the southeastern side the edge of the Forest rises sharply above the Severn Estuary along the fringe of which lay the main line between Gloucester and South Wales. Three small railways ran down from the Forest to the estuary. The most northerly was the former Forest of Dean Branch (originally known as the Bullo Pill Railway and authorized as early as 1809), which reached the main line at Bullo Pill Junction near Newnham. It served Cinderford and was connected with several collieries. At Awre Junction, further south, the former Forest of Dean Central Railway, some 4¾ miles in length, connected other collieries with the main line, and at Lydney the former Severn & Wye Junction Railway (G.W. & M.R. Joint) stretched through the centre of the Forest to Lydbrook, on the northern fringe, where it made the fourth exit from the Forest by connecting with the Ross and Monmouth line in the valley of the Wye. The fifth line, now abandoned, connected Coleford (which was also linked up with the Severn & Wye Junction Railway) with the Monmouth–Chepstow line at Wyesham Junction in the Wye valley.

Now since the central part of the Forest lies at 500 feet and more, all of these lines have to make steep descents to the surrounding lowlands, and every one of them uses the valley of an immature stream to do so, because, steep and sinuous as these valleys are, they have cut back through the rim of the Basin to provide access to the heart of the Forest.

Sometimes a very striking contrast is apparent between the upper (mature) and lower (rejuvenated) sections of the same valley. The upper part of Allan Water is formed by a number of small streams which flow northwards from the western end of the Ochil Hills to coalesce and turn sharply westwards near Blackford. This little town is situated at the head of the broad, flat valley of Strath Allan, which is connected north-eastwards by a col with the larger valley of Strath Earn. The main line from Perth to Stirling enters Strath Allan through this col near Gleneagles Station (Fig. 4). From the summit (422 feet), which lies approximately where it is crossed by the Dunfermline–Crieff road, the line falls gently into the Strath, the floor of which is drained

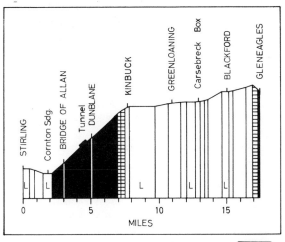

Gradients : 1/100 and steeper

Between 1/101 & 1/150

Less steep than 1/151

FIG. 4. GRADIENT PROFILE OF PART OF THE STIRLING–PERTH MAIN LINE (FORMER CALEDONIAN RAILWAY), IN STRATH ALLAN, PERTHSHIRE

Based on 'Gradients of the British Main Line Railways'

by a meandering river and in places by straighter channels artificially cut to improve the impeded drainage. The gentle fall of the river is matched by the equally gentle gradients of the railway, the profile of which closely resembles that of an ideal mature river. Below Blackford there is a mile at 1 in 165, then a gradual diminution of gradient by Carsebreck Signal Box, after which the steepest gradient is 1 in 514 followed by nearly two miles of level track to Kinbuck which marks, as it were, the base-level to which it is graded. In terms of drainage Kinbuck represents the knick-point in the rejuvenated Allan Water, and this is paralleled on the railway by a sudden steepening as the line enters the rejuvenated valley section and begins the descent which it maintains

G.C.—D

at gradients between 1 in 74 and 1 in 100 as far as the alluvium of the Forth valley beyond Bridge of Allan. In this section there is a marked increase not only in the steepness of the gradients but also in the frequency and severity of the curves and engineering works, which include several rock-cuttings, bridges, and a tunnel.

Everywhere in central Scotland where railways follow the valleys of rejuvenated streams the same features are to be found— either twisting and steeply graded lines as at Colinton on the Water of Leith, or lines which use only the upper valley-sides, usually only for short distances. But far more often these rejuvenated river-valleys are shunned by railways altogether. The River Clyde after being followed (with minor deviations) in its mature upper course by the main line of the former Caledonian Railway (Plate 5), turns sharply south-west near Carstairs and before reaching Lanark plunges into a gorge, reproducing on a somewhat grander scale the features of rejuvenation already illustrated in the Allan Water. All the tributaries which join the main stream below this knick-point are in process of being regraded to their respective base-levels at the points of confluence with the main stream and exhibit marked features of rejuvenation themselves. Some of them, the North Calder is an example, are followed by railways in their upper (mature) sections but never below the knick-point, except on the Nethan below Lesmahagow and the Avon near Stonehouse where the lines concerned are high up, in fact nearer the plateau surface than the valley-bottom, and follow these upper slopes only for very short distances. With these partial exceptions the generalization holds good for every one of these rivers including the North, South, and 'Rotten' Calders, the Garrion and Fiddler Burns, the Mouse Water, and the Rivers Nethan and Avon, and this in spite of the fact that the area is one of high population-density, is part of a coalfield which has long been the site of considerable industrial activity and is a district served by a railway network as dense as any in Scotland except in the immediate environs of Glasgow and Edinburgh. A study of the similar rejuvenated river-valleys leading to the southern side of the Forth would give results almost as striking.

While the conclusion that rejuvenated valleys are physically unsuited to easy railway construction naturally follows from these examples and indeed is valid, it is not the whole story. One is bound to add that these valleys have also tended to prove unsuitable for the growth of the larger settlements which contain

Photo: Aerofilms

PLATE 5. ELVANFOOT, LANARKSHIRE

Two of the headwaters of the Clyde, the Daer Water (left) and Potrail Water (right), rise in the Lowther Hills and converge (towards the camera) in the middle distance. Although it owes much to glacial influence, Upper Clydesdale exhibits most of the features associated with 'maturity' in landscape evolution, in striking contrast with its lower section, below the Falls of Clyde, some 20 miles further north. The Glasgow–Carlisle road (A.74) in the foreground and the former Caledonian Railway, after following the main valley upstream through Abington and Crawford, make for the small tributary valley of the Clydes Burn, entering left, and follow this for about two miles to reach Beattock Summit, where a through pass gives access to the Annan drainage-system. On the right of the valley can be seen another main road (A.702) which leads through the Lowther Hills to Nithsdale and Dumfries, following approximately the route of the Roman road. Vestiges of the latter can be seen some 200 yards inside the sharp bend in the road. The patch of light-coloured ground which flanks the Dumfries road, crossing from one side to the other near the first meander loop in the river, marks the route of the pipeline from the reservoir in the upper part of the Daer valley.

The railway diverging from the main line at Elvanfoot Station (right) and terminating short of the main road, is the 'stump' of the light railway to the lead-mining area of Leadhills and Wanlockhead, the abandoned track of which can be seen curving back into the valley of another small tributary, the Elvan Water.

It is the widespread occurrence of valleys of this kind which has made the crossing of the Southern Uplands a comparatively simple task. View to the south.

the population and the principal industrial sites (including most of the collieries), and since these tend to occupy the upper surfaces above the rejuvenated gorges the railways have in turn tended to serve them.

To return to the minor landforms associated with mature valleys, it has been pointed out that three elements, valley-side, terrace, and flood-plain, commonly provide complementary level surfaces for the development of communications, and some examples of these may now be considered with particular reference to railways. The distinction between the three elements is not necessarily of great significance to the railway engineer, even where such differences may have been quite sharp enough to affect the location of settlement profoundly. This is because the altitudinal differences between them are not necessarily great. Valley settlements are usually more closely related to the disposition of ground-water, soils, etc. than to altitude as such. Therefore they may be very precisely related to the occurrence of river-gravels, and yet in the same valley the flood-plain and terraces may be so nearly at the same level as to make it quite easy for a railway to pass periodically from one landform to the other. Indeed a study of almost any mature valley carrying a railway will show that the frequent transgression of the boundaries between flood-plain, terrace (if present), and valley-side is the normal thing, but where long stretches of comparatively uninterrupted terrace exist, they may be followed for several miles at a stretch.

The Trent valley may be taken as an example. The line of the former Midland Railway from Nottingham to Lincoln follows it as far as Newark, but in this section the river-terrace, though of wide occurrence, tends to be fragmentary, and furthermore the fragments frequently form the sites of settlements.[3] The railway, therefore, makes much use of the alluvium of the flood-plain. A little below Newark, however, the former Great Northern main line, which follows the western side of the valley by Muskham and Carlton, keeps almost entirely to the terraces. Similarly, further upstream in the Burton district there is a well-developed and fairly continuous river-terrace on the left bank (the Beeston Terrace[4]), and the Derby–Birmingham line, as it runs through

[3] K. M. Clayton, 'The geomorphology of the area around Nottingham and Derby'. *E. Mids. Geog.* No. 3 (June 1953), p. 16.
[4] K. M. Clayton, 'The glacial chronology of part of the Middle Trent Basin'. *P.G.A.* 64 (1953), p. 198.

the Trent valley by Burton to Wichnor Junction, is almost confined to it. In contrast again, for the last six miles into Birmingham this railway follows the quite narrow strip of alluvium of the Rea–Tame flood-plain, where the terraces, though present, are very patchy.

In the Thames valley, where the terraces are a conspicuous feature of the scenery, there are instances of railways following terraces continuously for two or three miles. Indeed by the former Southern Railway route to Windsor it is possible to travel the whole way from Waterloo without leaving the flood-plain terrace except to cross the Taplow Terrace between Twickenham and Feltham and a few ribbons of alluvium fringing the Thames and its small tributaries, but this is quite exceptional.

To revert to the more usual case where the railway crosses frequently from one landform to another, this may be simply the outcome of their irregularity of occurrence, and if this is so any railway line is bound to pass from one to the other in order to maintain a reasonably straight course. But sometimes a railway will be diverted by some definite obstacle from what appears to be its obvious course. Mention has already been made of the settlement sites of the Trent valley. A good example of interference with the potential course of a railway comes from the Wylye valley (Wiltshire). For several miles above Wilton the right bank of the flood-plain is flanked by a river-terrace, and this is used by the railway where possible. But it also happens to provide the best sites for settlements, and where these occur, as at Stockton, Wylye, Hanging Langford, Little Langford, and Great Wishford (Plate 6), the line passes *above* the settlements, crossing on to the Chalk which here forms the solid rock of the valley-sides. The terrace does not cease to exist at these points. It is simply not available for this particular type of land use.

At Oxford, where the Cherwell joins the Isis-Thames, the land between the two rivers consists mainly of part of the Summertown–Radley (or 'Second') Terrace, fairly level and raised above the flood-plain. But since it formed the site of the city it was not available for the railway, which had to keep to the undeveloped alluvium on the western side. Here, at a point where the main road leaving Oxford for the West crossed the alluvium, the two companies concerned built their stations.

On the eastern side of London the main line to Colchester and Ipswich, between its original Shoreditch terminus and Manor

Park, follows the flood-plain terrace, but this is breached by the alluvium of the River Lea which crosses it on its way to join the Thames. At this point the original Cambridge line diverged to follow the Lea valley northwards, and this valley fixed the point of junction with the Colchester line at Stratford. But the terrace

Photo: J. K. St. Joseph, by permission of the Committee for Aerial Photography, University of Cambridge, and of the Air Ministry Crown Copyright Reserved

PLATE 6. GREAT WISHFORD, WILTSHIRE

The Salisbury–Westbury line of the former Great Western Railway is seen (left) following the Wylye valley above Wilton. Leaving the river-terrace, which is here occupied by the twin settlements of Great Wishford (left) and Stoford (right), it passes on to the Chalk which forms the valley-side, even though this has necessitated the making of a cutting. View to the north-west.

on either side of the Lea alluvium provided better and more valuable building-land than the alluvium itself, which had therefore been neglected for building and was more cheaply available for other purposes. So the large system of carriage-sidings, etc., now occupies a considerable area of land on this strip of alluvium which separates the two sections of the terrace.

One must not suppose, then, that the mere existence of a physical path is of paramount importance; railways often have to be content with what is left over after the requirements of other land users have been met.

A common obstacle to railway-building in a mature valley results from river meanders crossing from one side of the flood-plain to the other, and if frequent bridging is necessary it may greatly increase the expense of building the line. Thus the main line between Berwick and Edinburgh, which for a short distance follows the mature valley of the Eye Water, crosses it seven times in four miles between Reston and Grantshouse, while the Derby–Manchester main line in the neighbourhood of Belper and Matlock crosses the much larger Derwent eleven times in eleven miles. This kind of difficulty is not, of course, confined to mature valleys. The point is that the attainment of maturity does not necessarily eliminate the expense of frequent bridging. It often happens that the meander-belt stretches right up to the valley-sides, thereby increasing the difficulty of outflanking it. Just to the north of Bedford the main line of the former Midland Railway makes use of a portion of the Ouse valley. The valley-sides are quite sharply delimited and the railway keeps almost along the middle of the flood-plain, which is crossed backwards and forwards by the meander loops, so that there are six bridges of appreciable size in $5\frac{1}{2}$ miles. Where the expense is not too great it may be preferable in a case like this to divert the course of the river and thereby cut out some of the meanders. This has been done, for instance, between Wakefield and Normanton, where the Manchester & Leeds Railway Company diverted a meander of the Calder to save building two bridges on its main line. This resulted in the creation of an artificial ox-bow lake which can still be seen (Grid Ref. 44/357209).

To revert to the Bedford example it is interesting to note that the main road (A.6), with its greater freedom to rise and fall, manages to outflank the meanders of the Ouse and so avoids the necessity of bridging it at all in this section north of Bedford.

Where meanders have been incised they offer a particular kind of problem to the railway engineer. If the swing of the meanders is sufficiently gentle, it may be possible for a railway to follow them, especially if the river has, by lateral corrasion, broadened its valley-floor. But where the meanders are too pronounced the line may be able to make only a limited use of the valley, tunnelling through the intervening spurs to pass from one section of the valley to another. One of the best known examples of incised meanders occurs where the River Wye cuts into the Carboniferous Limestone on the north-western edge of the Forest of Dean. For most of its course the Ross–Monmouth–Chepstow line follows the meanders, but at Welsh Bicknor and Symond's Yat the river curves are too severe and tunnels have had to be bored to give access from one loop to the next, while at the southern extremity the steep-sided curves approaching Chepstow Castle have been avoided altogether by tunnelling through the left flank of the valley to reach the main line at Wye Junction, instead of following the river right into the town.

Where the nature of the traffic permits in building railways recourse may be had to the use of a narrower gauge, which enables sharper curves to be used. The River Manifold in Staffordshire, for instance, pursues an extremely winding course below Hulme End and is bounded by steep and in places precipitous limestone cliffs. The river has succeeded in developing a narrow ribbon of level land, but even so the meanders are so sharp that it would scarcely be possible to carry a standard-gauge railway along the valley without very extensive tunnelling through the limestone spurs. When in 1904 the railway was opened from Waterhouses to Hulme End, it followed throughout the whole of its course the valley of the Manifold and its tributary the Hamps, which exhibits very similar features. The line was built purely for local traffic, mainly small-scale mineral traffic, and a narrow gauge was not incompatible with this. By employing a gauge of 2 feet 6 inches it was found to be quite practicable to follow the valley-bottom with comparatively little tunnelling.

Other examples of railways following incised meanders can be found, such as in the Dee valley above Llangollen, but usually they are to be found where the incision is so deep and the surrounding uplands so high that it would be difficult to find an alternative route. At Durham, for instance, although the incised meander which almost encircles the old city is very spectacular, the plateau into which it is incised is not much above 300 feet and the railways have found it possible, though perhaps not easy, to avoid the Wear valley. The original main line kept well to the east of the river, passing through Sherburn, and when later the present main line was opened it used the complicated system of tributaries on the south-western side of the city to reach the present Durham Station on the western side.

Both upstream and downstream from Durham incised meanders

are typical of the River Wear (Plate 7), and it is significant that, while its general trend is followed by the railways from Bishop Auckland to Durham and from Durham to Sunderland, the valley-bottom is not followed at all by any railway below Witton Park.

Photo: Aerofilms

PLATE 7. RAILWAY VIADUCT, NEAR LEAMSIDE, CO. DURHAM

The incised meanders of the post-glacial Wear are useless for the passage of railways, whereas the surfaces into which they are cut provide a comparatively suitable platform. The Durham–Sunderland line is here seen crossing the Wear in its passage over such a surface. View looking north-north-east.

In the valleys so far considered running water is the agent which has been primarily responsible for their formation. There are significant differences when we come to those valleys which owe their dominant features to the work of ice. The distinction is not merely one of academic interest to the geomorphologists. There are certain characteristic qualities which moving ice imparts to a landscape and which have a far-reaching influence on the communications. No attempt is made here to discuss the controversies about the mechanism whereby these features are made. It may well be that in the majority of cases the ice merely modified pre-existing water-eroded valleys. The point is that it did modify them and in such a way as sometimes to impede, sometimes to assist, the passage of communications.

Among the difficulties created by glaciation may be mentioned the steepness of the heads of some typical glaciated valleys, the formation of steps in a valley-bottom which may result from the increased load of ice at the confluence of glaciers, and the legacy of lakes, moraines, and other obstacles which are left behind in the valley-bottom, but which rarely constitute more than a minor obstruction. To these one may add the hanging valleys which are common where tributary streams enter the main valleys and also the numerous features such as corries, arêtes, shattered rock faces, pyramidal peaks, and so on, which are typical of glaciated summits but which, from the very nature of their occurrence, are rarely relevant to the development of communication, at any rate in Britain.

It is fair to say that the difficulties mentioned above are more than compensated for by the 'smoothing-out' of ice-action in a valley. Where in a water-worn valley overlapping spurs have existed, they tend to be truncated by the glacier and the valley-sides are thereby straightened out. Furthermore there results from the occupation of a valley by a glacier a major change in its cross-profile which becomes characteristically U-shaped in section, and this has important implications from the point of view of railway-building. Finally there are the well-known through-valleys, the exact origin of which is still a matter of controversy, but which recent workers are increasingly inclined to attribute to glacial action,[5] and which have had a profound effect on communications in glaciated uplands, particularly, of course, in the Scottish Highlands.

Where erosion has been carried out primarily by a true valley glacier and not by ice moving into it over a water-parting, the valley-head is often steep and difficult to surmount. The Lake District possesses many glacial features of this kind but only occasionally does one find modern communications using such valleys as through routes. Most of the well-known passes which carry motor roads, such as Honister, Wrynose, and Kirkstone, occur at the heads of glaciated valleys of this kind, though again there is generally evidence of ice passing over the cols at least during some phase of the glaciation. In many similar valleys,

[5] G. H. Dury, 'Diversion of drainage by ice'. *Science News*, No. 38, pp. 48–71. Penguin (1955).

Photo: *Aerofilms*

PLATE 8. STRATH TAY, PERTHSHIRE

A combination of glaciation, alluvial infilling and normal erosion in this section
of the Tay valley has provided the railway engineer with an ideal opportunity
to penetrate the south-eastern fringe of the Highlands. Flood-plain and terraces
produce a broad valley-floor and the meander-belt is confined to one side of it.
In the middle distance the line (Perth–Inverness) swings across to take up a
position on the other side, but there is no serious obstacle to be encountered for
several miles. The second-class road from Birnam to Aberfeldy (B.898, left)
clings to the boundary between the valley-side and the lower terraces. A
remnant of a higher terrace can be seen (left) but is too fragmentary to be used
by the communications which in any case have no need here to forsake the
valley-floor. In more difficult circumstances terrace fragments of this sort may
be extremely useful. The main road to the north of Scotland (A.9) is marked by
the broad black shadow where it passes through the coniferous forest (right).
A fragment of General Wade's military road can be seen lower down, almost
on the river-bank.

The Tay is at this point about to enter a gorge section through which the
railway can pass only with the help of cuttings, embankments, and one of the
very few tunnels to be found in the Highlands. The main road (unlike General
Wade's road) has left the valley-bottom in order that it may take advantage of a
small col (right foreground), thereby avoiding the bottom of the defile altogether. The maintenance of two motor roads has been encouraged by the fact
that the Tay is unbridged for some twelve miles above Dunkeld. Each side of
the river therefore requires its own communications. View to the north-north-
west.

where the motor roads stop short of the valley-heads, ancient trackways continue, climbing steeply to reach passes such as those of Nan Bield, Sty Head, and Esk Hause. In Ennerdale, perhaps the most perfect of the U-shaped valleys of the Lake District, the head of the valley rises into the summits of Great and Green Gable, but on either side of the valley-head lower passages permit the old pack-horse track to reach Buttermere (Scarth Gap) and Wastdale (Black Sail).

The efficacy of the Scottish Highlands as barriers to communications has been greatly mitigated by the existence of a liberal sprinkling of through-valleys which connect the principal drainage systems and which afford routeways so easy (considering the mountainous country) that in the whole of the Highlands it is impossible to find a single example of a summit-tunnel connecting one main drainage system with another.[6] It is no exaggeration to say that these through-valleys have made possible the provision of railways (and greatly facilitated penetration by roads) in the Highlands, though at the cost of much deviation. It is doubtful whether the expectation of traffic from this lean countryside could ever have justified the expense of making the long tunnels which would otherwise have been unavoidable.

The use of through-valleys, both by road and rail, is one of the most obvious features of the geography of the Highlands and is one of the few aspects of the physical basis of railway geography which have been fully recognized,[7] although the part played in their formation by transfluent ice has only recently been understood.[8] What is equally important and much less obvious is the significance of the glaciated valleys by which these passages are approached. Two or three examples from Argyll and Western Perthshire will make this clear.

The line from Oban eastwards, after following the side of Loch Awe, uses the valley of the River Lochy to reach Tyndrum, where a through-valley at just over 800 feet gives access to the east-flowing drainage of Strath Fillan (Fig. 5). For most of its length the floor of Glen Lochy is falling westwards with remarkable

[6] There are a few short tunnels connecting minor tributary valleys of the same drainage system, e.g. on the West Highland railway to Mallaig, but in no instance is an important water-parting pierced by tunnel.
[7] See, for instance, A. Stevens, 'The Highlands and Hebrides', in A. G. Ogilvie, *Great Britain: Essays in Regional Geography* (1937).
[8] D. L. Linton, 'Some Scottish river-captures re-examined'. *S.G.M.* 65 (1949), p. 123; 67 (1951), p. 31; 70 (1954), p. 64. Also G. H. Dury, 'A glacial breach in the North-west Highlands'. *S.G.M.* 69 (1953), p. 106.

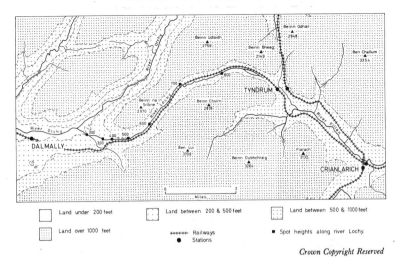

F*ig*. 5. RAILWAYS AND DRAINAGE-SYSTEMS ON THE ARGYLL–
PERTHSHIRE BORDER

regularity at about 50 feet per mile (or roughly 1 in 100), and in
the upper part of the glen the railway has no difficulty in following it. But as Glen Lochy approaches the larger valley of Glen
Orchy, there is a marked valley-step (Glen Lochy being in other
words a hanging tributary valley), involving a fall of some 400
feet in just over two miles, quite an impossible gradient for a main-
line railway, and the problem is therefore how to lift the line up
to the top of this step from the level of Loch Awe. The significance
of the U-shaped valley now becomes apparent. At Dalmally the
railway leaves the valley-bottom and begins to make height by
climbing obliquely up the valley-side, which, owing to the straight
contours and gentle cross-profile is quite easy, so that, by the time
it reaches the valley-step, it is level with the top of it and can thus
enter the more gently graded section of Glen Lochy.

Beyond Tyndrum the railway follows Strath Fillan, and as far
as Crianlarich the West Highland line (Glasgow to Fort William
and Mallaig) runs parallel with it. The contrast between these
two railways illustrates the adaptability of a glaciated valley for
carrying railways. The Oban line is making for the through-valley
west of Tyndrum, which lies only a few feet above the floor of the
strath, and this it can reach quite easily without rising appreciably above the river-level. The Fort William line, on the other
hand, leaves the strath to the north of Tyndrum 183 feet higher,

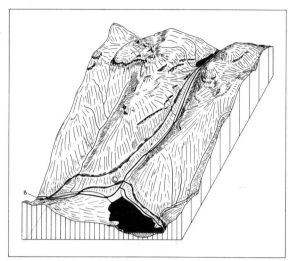

Fɪɢ. 6. RAILWAYS AND VALLEYS NEAR LOCHEARNHEAD, PERTHSHIRE

Block diagram as seen from the south-east. The lake in the foreground is Loch Earn. B = Balquhidder. L = Lochearnhead. G = Glenoglehead.

and between Crianlarich and Tyndrum it is climbing steadily by an oblique gradient up the valley-side. In other words, although the two through-valleys concerned require approach-routes from the south-east at different altitudes, their requirements can both be met by Strath Fillan, thanks to the straightness of its valley-sides and the nature of its cross-profile, both characteristic products of glaciation.

The last example from this district is Glen Ogle, which affords perhaps the best illustration in Britain of the use of a glaciated valley as an approach to a pass. The Callander & Oban line, after following the sides of Loch Lubnaig, has to pass from the valley of Strathyre into Glen Dochart, one of the headwater valleys of the Tay. To do so it has to make use, for a few miles, of the headwaters of the Earn drainage system around the western end of Loch Earn (Fig. 6). This involves the use of two through-valleys, (a) between Strathyre and Lochearnhead at Balquhidder Station, and (b) between Lochearnhead and Glen Dochart at Glenoglehead. The altitudes concerned are a little under 500 feet at Balquhidder and 942 feet at Glenoglehead, but between them the ground-level falls to about 320 feet at the alluvium round the head of the loch. If it were necessary, by following the valley-bottom, to lose 150 feet or so from Balquhidder to Lochearnhead, the steepness of the climb from Lochearnhead to Glenoglehead would be quite pro- hibitive and Glen Dochart could be reached only by a long tunnel under the Glenoglehead divide. But owing to the configuration of Glen Ogle, which is a beautiful example of a glaciated valley, with smooth, straight sides, it is possible to carry the line well up the valley-side above Lochearnhead, thereby maintaining and gradu- ally increasing the altitude of the line from Balquhidder to Glen- oglehead. It has proved quite practicable to achieve this by cutting a narrow nick or shelf in the western side of Glen Ogle.

Many similar examples could be found in Scotland to support the hypothesis that glaciation tends to facilitate the penetration of uplands by railways, and even where it has left a legacy of ob- stacles in the valley-bottoms it has at the same time provided the means of overcoming them by making it possible for the railway to rise up the valley-side above them.

The exploitation of this kind of opportunity by roads is perhaps less impressive in Britain owing to the fact that their use of steeper gradients permits them to keep to the valley-bottoms longer than can the railways. Nevertheless this process of diagonal climbing above glaciated valleys can be seen in many examples. Two from Snowdonia will suffice.

The road which runs north-eastwards from Beddgelert (A.498) follows the valley of Nant-Gwynant and makes for the Capel Curig– Llanberis road (A.4086) at the head of the valley (Pen-y-Gwrhyd). The valley-floor rises very slowly and at Llyn Gwynant is at only 217 feet (lake surface). From the head of the lake in the first mile it rises about 80 feet and in the second mile over 550 feet. This is much too steep for a modern motor road, but by leaving the valley-bottom at Llyn Gwynant and spreading the climb over the whole distance up to the summit it is able to reach its destination at a gradient which is quite reasonable even for heavy motor traffic. As one climbs above the valley-floor one can look down to see the old road keeping nearer the valley-bottom and tackling the final climb up to Pen-y-Gwrhyd at a very much steeper gradient. This valley, incidentally, figures prominently in the paper in which W. M. Davis elaborated his views on the effects of glaciation on an upland,[9] and exhibits the orthodox features of a glaciated valley to a marked degree.

The other example from this area illustrates the surmounting

[9] W. M. Davis, 'Glacial erosion in North Wales'. *Q.J.G.S.* lxv (1909), p. 281.

of a valley-step by a road in much the same way as the Oban
railway surmounts the step of Glen Lochy. The feature is described
by Trueman in these terms:

> This straight and simple section (the lower part) of the Nant
> Ffrancon valley ends at Rhaiadr Ogwen in a sharp step, the valley
> floor having that exaggeratedly stepped profile which is produced by
> ice action. Travelling up the pass the valley here seems to end suddenly
> against a high rocky cliff; down this the river falls in a most beautiful
> cascade, escaping from Llyn Ogwen, situated almost immediately
> above the fall, by a shallow gorge, where great masses of ice-smoothed
> rock form bare mounds.[10]

All glaciated valleys have their own individual characteristics,
and the Nant Ffrancon has some unusual features associated with
apparent reversals of drainage above Llyn Ogwen, so that one
should hesitate to describe it as a 'typical glaciated valley', but
the section immediately below the step exhibits just those features
of straight sides and a U-shaped cross-profile to which the word
'typical' would be appropriate enough, and here again it is precisely those features which enable the road (A.5) to make height
gradually and reach Rhaiadr Ogwen with comparatively little
difficulty. A comparison between the incipient post-glacial gorge
which the river has cut into the valley-step and the smooth configuration of the main valley illustrates vividly the contrast
between the two valley-forms as potential carriers of communications.

Reference has been made to the step features in the floors of
glaciated valleys. Similar features are often to be found in an even
more exaggerated form where larger glaciated valleys are joined
by small tributary valleys. Where the floor of the tributary valley
is at a much higher level than that of the main valley it is described
as 'hanging'. This is what had happened in Glen Lochy which could
be described as a 'hanging' tributary of the larger Glen Orchy. In so
far as these hanging valleys represent tributaries of main valleys
which have been more effectively deepened by ice, they may be
regarded as the glacial equivalents of the rejuvenated valleys referred to in the last chapter. Indeed in some cases the process of
rejuvenation cannot be divorced from glacial overdeepening in the
main valley and the creation of a new base level which is the
essential characteristic of rejuvenation. Where the 'hanging' effect
is very well marked, roads or railways may encounter real diffi-

[10] A. E. Trueman, *Geology and Scenery in England and Wales*. Pelican (1949), p. 213.

culty in getting up into the hanging valley and yet find a comparatively easy path once over the step. The road from Derwentwater to Watendlath (Cumberland) is a case in point. The Watendlath Beck flows in a smooth-sided, gently sloping valley by the
hamlet of Watendlath until it reaches the step at Lodore, down
which it plunges in the Lodore Falls. In the upper part of the
valley the old track keeps close to the beck in the valley-bottom,
but before the falls are reached it leaves the beck and makes its
way down diagonally through the wooded slopes on the eastern
side of Derwentwater, crossing the valley of the next beck (Barrow
Beck) in the process.

A good example of a railway line tackling a similar problem
can be found again in North Wales, in the hanging valley of Cwm
Croesor, which the narrow-gauge slate railway from Portmadoc
could only reach by a steep incline, above which it levelled off in
the flatter part of the Croesor valley.

A mere statement that a valley has been glaciated does not
indicate how far it owes its characteristics to the agency of ice.
There are, in fact, degrees of glaciation. The valley of the River
Clydach, which joins the Usk a few miles above Abergavenny, is
technically a glaciated valley, according to Strahan and Gibson,[11]
in so far as it contains boulder-clay and is thought to have diverted
eastwards the ice which would otherwise have entered the head of
the valley of the Ebbw Fach. But the intensity and/or duration of
glaciation has been insufficient to impart the appearance of a
glaciated landform. The valley is referred to in the *Memoirs*[12] as a
'rocky ravine' even in this drift-bearing section. Add to this the
fact that further excavation of the river-bed has almost certainly
taken place in post-glacial times, and one is left with a valley
which still exhibits many of the features of youth, with formidable
consequences for the construction of both road (A.465) and railway (the Merthyr, Tredegar & Abergavenny line of the former
L.N.W.R.). The latter climbs steadily at gradients of 1 in 34 to
1 in 37.

In addition to the glacial valleys there are others which,
though never occupied by the ice, nevertheless owe their origin
to glaciation. These are the glacial spillways or overflow-channels
carved by running water which has been diverted from its natural

---

[11] A. Strahan and W. Gibson, *Memoirs of the Geological Survey of England and Wales.*
The Geology of the South Wales Coalfield. Part II, Abergavenny (2nd ed. 1927).
[12] ibid. p. 107.

course by an obstruction of ice. Valleys of this sort, owing to their mode of origin, have a very particular part to play in the geography of communications, and particularly of railways.

Perhaps the best example in Britain comes from north-east Yorkshire where the overflow-channel of Newton Dale has been carved out some 300 feet below the level of the North Yorkshire Moors. This spillway was formed during a period when an ice-sheet over what is now the North Sea impinged on these moors, blocking the valleys of the eastward-flowing streams and thereby creating large glacial lakes. The water of these lakes rose until it reached the lowest point at which it could overflow across the inter-fluve into the next valley. Once the escape-channel had been located, downward erosion began and was often very vigorous if the quantities of water were large. Only if the ice-sheet dwindled in size enough to expose a lower outlet further down the valley was the first escape-channel abandoned.

In the case of Newton Dale a lake was formed in Eskdale, a lake which in turn was probably being fed by other channels carrying water diverted from further north as well as melt-water off the ice-sheet itself. The waters of Lake Eskdale rose until they began to overflow to the south into the Vale of Pickering.[13] It is not known how long this outlet was used, but it lasted long enough to leave behind a very clearly defined trough, at present occupied by two quite small streams, the Pickering Beck flowing southwards and the Eller Beck flowing northwards. At the water-parting the valley-floor is so flat that it is difficult to see exactly where the divide is situated. Yet the whole valley is at this point extremely well developed and was obviously formed by water running right through. From its northern end near Grosmont to its opening into the Vale of Pickering it is followed by the railway (Whitby & Pickering of 1833). The course of the railway is completely dictated by the line of this overflow-channel, but for which it would have to climb two or three hundred feet higher and pass over the upper surfaces of the moorlands, a feat which would very likely have proved so difficult as to prevent its construction at all (Plate 9).

The reason why valleys of this sort assume so much importance, at least locally, is directly related to their mode of origin. They mark the position of what was, at least for a time, the lowest available passage between two drainage-systems. But any railway

[13] P. F. Kendall and H. E. Wroot, *The Geology of Yorkshire* (1924), Chapter 42.

Photo: Brian Fisher

PLATE 9. NEWTON DALE, YORKSHIRE

The glacial overflow-channel of Newton Dale, seen here from Newton-upon-Rawcliffe, carried the Whitby–Pickering line through the Jurassic hills of north-east Yorkshire, which, however, can be crossed by the main road at much higher elevations. Indeed the spillway was almost entirely devoid of roads until afforestation brought about new requirements. The white scar in the distance marks the line of a Forestry Commission road. View to the north-north-west.

passing between two drainage-systems tends to make use of the lowest available passage, provided that on other grounds it is adequate. Consequently it is by no means unusual or fortuitous to find railways using glacial overflow-channels for this purpose. Other examples can be found in the system of channels further south than Newton Dale but in a comparable situation, for instance between Hunmanby and Speeton Stations, between Beverley and Market Weighton, and so on.

On the western side of the Pennines the glacial history has been worked out by Jowett.[14] There is a fine system of channels cut between the hills and what was at one time the ice-front. Parts of these can be picked out from the map by the line of reservoirs to the east of Chorley. The railway from Chorley to Blackburn

[14] A. Jowett, 'The glacial geology of East Lancashire'. *Q.J.G.S.* lxx (1914), p. 199.

follows one of them at Brinscall. At various times the level of the water rose so high that it found an escape route right across the Pennine watershed and into the Calder valley near Todmorden. The two gorges of Walsden and Cliviger were formed by the escaping water, and the influence of these on the location of communications hereabouts is very evident. The Cliviger gorge carries the Todmorden–Burnley railway (opened 1849) and the A.646 road. The Walsden gorge carries the Todmorden–Littleborough road (A.6033), the Rochdale Canal, and the line of the Manchester & Leeds Railway. Although the railway passes below the summit in a tunnel, the lines of its approaches are determined by the position of the spillway no less than are those of the road and canal.

Much the same could be said of the Harecastle tunnels in North Staffordshire. Here the Trent and Mersey Canal and the North Staffordshire Railway are both carried in tunnels under the main watershed of England, a little below the level of a well-developed overflow-channel, the exit from the northern end of which would have been too steep for surface lines. Not far to the south-west the main line from Euston to Crewe crosses what would otherwise be a difficult barrier by means of the overflow-channel at Whitmore.

Another spectacular example is to be seen at Ferryhill (Co. Durham). Here the escarpment of the Magnesian Limestone, which forms a prominent feature cutting right across the county from Sunderland towards Bishop Auckland, has been breached by a steep-sided overflow-channel. This is the only point where the water-parting between the Wear and the Tees drainage-systems can be crossed at a height of less than 400 feet. Its use by the railway goes back to early days. In 1834 the Clarence Railway, which was in vigorous competition with the slightly earlier Stockton & Darlington Railway as a conveyor of coals from the South Durham coalfield to the Tees estuary, opened a branch by which it obtained access to the collieries in the area around Spennymoor and Coxhoe. To reach these it had to cross the escarpment, and the passage which obviously suggested itself was the Ferryhill overflow-channel. It was not until some years later (1844) that the Darlington–Gateshead line was completed, and this, too, followed the overflow-channel, the influence of which can immediately be seen from a glance at the Ordnance Survey one-inch map (sheet 85, Durham). The two lines can be seen converging on the gap from the directions of Stockton and Darlington. In the gap itself they run parallel for a mile and three-quarters.[15] Then in the course of the next mile and a quarter five fingers spread out over the Coal Measures. The Bishop Auckland branch runs through a right angle west to Spennymoor. The present main line continues north then bears left to Croxdale. The earlier main line keeps in a more northerly direction to Sherburn. The little Coxhoe branch leads north-east towards the limestone quarries near Quarrington Hill; and finally the line through Cornforth, Trimdon, and Castle Eden cuts back across the escarpment by a much more difficult route towards the sea at Hartlepool.

In all these examples, in which railways are seeking to pass from one valley-system to another, the glacial spillway comes to their aid. Where, however, they are based on a higher surface into which the diverted melt-waters have cut a trough across their path, then it follows that overflow-channels are not an advantage but an obstacle. Such a situation arose, for instance, on the Stanhope & Tyne Railway (Co. Durham), which was opened in 1834 from the limestone quarries near Stanhope in Weardale through the western part of the Durham coalfield at Annfield Plain to the Tyne at South Shields.

The western half of the line had to pass through country consisting of high but fairly level surfaces, much dissected by small tributaries of the Wear (such as the Waskerley Beck and Browney), the Team, and the Derwent. The only practicable course lay along the interfluves. At one phase during the retreat of the ice, the water, ponded back by ice in the Derwent valley, had found an escape into the head of the Browney valley and had carved the steep chasm of Hownes Gill, over 150 feet deep (Plate 10). Far from being helpful to the railway engineer, this formidable ravine presented a serious problem, and for some twenty-four years, until the viaduct was opened (1858), the wagons had to be lowered to the bottom and lifted up the other side by a rope-incline worked by a stationary engine—a complicated, not to say slow and expensive process, described in some detail by Tomlinson.[16] Here then the spillway was certainly an adversary rather than an ally.

In this brief review of glacial overflow-channels emphasis has necessarily been laid on the railways, since it is they which make most use of them. Not infrequently railways pass through overflow-

---

[15] A certain amount of cutting has been necessary within the gap, but the line of route has nevertheless been clearly dominated by the natural feature.

[16] W. W. Tomlinson, *The North Eastern Railway* (1914), pp. 244-5.

Photo: Aerofilms

PLATE 10. HOWNES GILL, CO. DURHAM

The comparatively level surface developed on the Coal Measures is indicated by the improved land. The wooded ravine of Hownes Gill is a glacial spillway connecting the Derwent (Tyne) and Browney (Wear) systems. The drainage of the land in the foreground is to the Derwent, while that beyond the viaduct is to the Browney through the wooded valley (left). A rough track, passing from one valley to the other, uses the spillway, but the railway, which is based on the higher surface, strides across from one side to the other. View to the south-east.

channels while the equivalent roads avoid them. In Ferryhill the Great North Road passes over the escarpment only a mile to the west of the overflow-channel which carries the railways. The Beverley–Market Weighton road also keeps to the top of the Chalk, unlike the railway. Much the same thing happens in the Tyne Gap. In all these cases the climb is not severe enough to preclude the road from the higher passage.

On the other hand the low-level routeway provided by an overflow-channel may, under particular local circumstances, furnish the opportunity needed by a road. Examples occur at Whitehaven, where the Workington road (A.595) uses one to climb out of the town, at Llanbedrog on the Lleyn Peninsula, and at several localities in Rossendale (Lancashire).

Even within this general category of 'valley routes', then, there is a great diversity of opportunity for the development of different kinds of communication. In the next chapter some other types of landform will be considered from a similar angle.

CHAPTER III

OTHER LANDFORMS AS ROUTEWAYS

The present configuration of the surface of Britain is the product of different forces acting on the rocks of which it is composed. It has been shown that some of these processes create channels suitable for accommodating lines of communication, but that often the landforms produced by river-erosion are not by any means ideal, and in this case it may be that other features of the land-surface can be found which will provide the necessary properties. The agents of erosion which fashion a landscape remind one of the chisel of a sculptor, whose work, when it is partly finished, still contains remnants of the original surface of the block of stone. In certain types of country it is possible to identify comparatively level surfaces not yet obliterated by the agents which are at present eating them away. In this country most such surfaces seem to be the result of earlier processes of denudation, having been produced by river-erosion or by the action of the sea and then subjected to further uplift. Sometimes these earlier cycles of erosion have only had time to become partly developed before further upward or downward movement took place. Sometimes evidence of many such surfaces can be found in the same locality. Sometimes all trace of them has been removed, and their former existence can only be inferred from the pattern of rivers which have worn them away.

The inferred existence of fragments of surfaces of this kind has been a challenge which has stimulated some of the most fruitful researches of British geomorphologists.[1] Over a wide area of south-east England many such fragments have been mapped, correlated, named and dated and have proved to be one of the chief keys in the elucidation of landscape-evolution. In some examples it is possible to discern quite precise associations between routeways and identified surface-remnants.[2] Practically all the

[1] e.g. S. W. Wooldridge and D. L. Linton, *Structure, Surface and Drainage in South-east England* (1955).
[2] The terms 'erosion-surface', 'erosion-platform', 'plateau', 'peneplain', etc., are all encountered in morphological descriptions of these features. 'Upland-plain' is pre-

remnants of the Mio-Pliocene peneplain in south-west Wiltshire,[3] for instance, carry roads or trackways, many of them being ancient. The Herepath (Salisbury Way) follows one of these on the northern side of the Ebble valley, while the larger fragment on the south side carried the Ridge Way known as the Ox Drove. Further to the north the Roman road from Sorbiodunum (Old Sarum) to the Mendips climbed rapidly from the Wylye valley a mile north of Wilton on to Grovely Hill, then followed a seven-mile strip of the Pliocene[4] marine plain before picking up the Mio-Pliocene surface of the Great Ridge north of Chicklade and Fonthill Bishop.

But the significance of these Tertiary surfaces to the student of communications is not quite what it is to the geomorphologist. To the latter they appear as tracts, dominantly linear in shape, but existing also in breadth up to a mile or more in places. Isolated and widely separated fragments, even though small, are of the greatest importance provided they can be identified as unimpaired portions of the upland-plain. Once denudation has lowered them beneath the initial surface they can no longer be so described. In the study of communications, however, it is their linear development which is important, and whether they represent true fragments of a particular surface is less relevant than whether they afford comparatively level routeways in the right direction. In short for our purposes we can include in these high-level routeways not only the actual relics of plains of marine and sub-aerial denudation, but also interfluves, cuestas, and ridges of various kinds, which may have suffered denudation in varying degrees, but are still recognizable as the antitheses of valley routeways.

Some of the most distinctive upland-plains are found in the south-western peninsula. The present drainage-systems have barely reached a stage of maturity and consist of rivers flowing well below the upland-surface in steep-sided and often winding valleys, of a type which has already been discussed. In Figure 7 a piece of country of this type is shown as it appears on the map. In the centre the remains of an upland-surface can be distinctly seen. It is mostly between 400 and 500 feet in height and is a part of the so-called 400-foot platform. Looked at from the east or the west

ferred by Wooldridge as being less controversial for use as a general term covering all nearly level upland-surfaces, irrespective of their mode of origin.

S. W. Wooldridge, 'The upland plains of Britain: their origin and geographical significance'. *Adv. of Sci.* vii, No. 26 (Sept. 1950), p. 162.

[3] Wooldridge and Linton, op. cit., pp. 38–40; see also their Fig. 10, p. 39.

[4] Now thought to be rather later in age. The term Plio-Pleistocene is perhaps more acceptable.

it would appear as a comparatively level skyline sloping gently seawards. It divides the tributaries of the Fowey River from those of the West Looe River. In both cases the tributaries are numerous

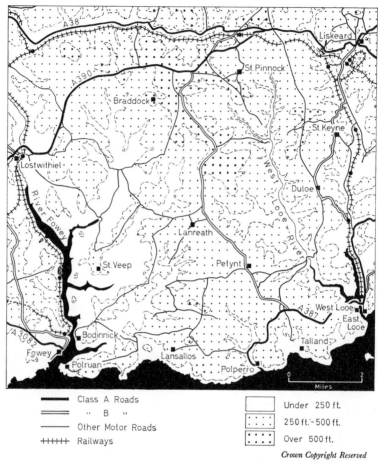

━━━━━ Class A Roads	▢ Under 250 ft.
═══ " B "	⠿ 250 ft.- 500 ft.
──── Other Motor Roads	⠿ Over 500 ft.
┼┼┼┼┼ Railways	

Crown Copyright Reserved

Fig. 7. THE ROADS OF THE FOWEY-LOOE AREA, CORNWALL

and all of them have cut down their valleys below the upland-plain, leaving small remnants of it projecting like promontories between each little valley. There is, in short, a main water-parting running north-south, and numerous minor water-partings running out from this, generally at right angles, though in detail their directions vary considerably. In the south the remnant is divided into two arms swinging south-west and south-east respectively, which are separated by the valleys of some small streams running towards the sea at Polperro and Talland.

Apart from the short section of road from West Looe to Polperro (A.387) there are no main roads in the area south of the Lostwithiel-Liskeard road (A.390), but of the minor roads the most important are related to the main watershed. Innumerable smaller roads, only the most important of which are shown in Figure 7, branch out from these to cover the whole area with a fine network, and the great majority of them keep to the minor water-partings. The resultant pattern is exactly the reverse of the patterns discussed in the preceding chapter, and there would seem to be three main reasons why this is so.

In the first place the river-valleys, particularly those of the smaller tributaries, exhibit many features indicative of youth, and are therefore not ideal as lines of communication. Secondly the roads are in most cases very old and have grown up largely to serve numerous rural settlements in an almost exclusively agricultural landscape, and these scattered settlements are more often than not situated on or near the upland-plain rather than in the valleys. Life is lived, one might say, nearer to the 400-foot contour than to sea-level, and from this point of view the upper surface naturally affords great opportunities for inter-communication between the settlements. Old village centres like Braddock, Lanreath, Pelynt, Lansallos, St. Veep, and Duloe are connected by roads which rise and fall very little, though one is bound to add that it is equally plausible to suggest that these village centres are the product of a high-level road pattern as to suppose that the roads have come into existence to serve the village centres. But to be uncertain as to whether the chicken or the egg came first is not to invalidate the proposition that the one habitually comes out of the other, and in this case the important thing is that road and settlement are related to each other and both are related to the surface of the upland-plain.

The third reason why the road-system has developed mainly on the upland-plain becomes apparent if one looks at the area just to the east of the Fowey River. Owing to the development of creeks, a road flanking the estuary would be forced further east, that is to say well within the area where the upland-remnants have to be crossed. There is just such a road from Lostwithiel through St. Veep to Bodinnick. But to reach this point it has to rise and fall well over 1,000 feet in aggregate, whereas the road through the centre of the area (B.3359), even allowing for the climb on to the 400-foot surface, has a total rise and fall which is very much less. It is in every way a more satisfactory route into the area.

This kind of road-system is extremely common, and all British uplands of moderate elevation furnish examples. Almost the whole

Photo: Aerofilms

PLATE 11. MICHELCOMBE, DEVON

'Youthful', wooded ravines and rounded interfluves here provide a contrast in the opportunities they afford for the development of minor roads; the advantages of the higher surfaces are obvious. Note the position of the hamlet where the roads come down from these higher surfaces to cross the stream. View looking west to Dartmoor.

of the south coast of Devon and Cornwall shows a similar type of road pattern (Plate 11). The Kingsbridge area is perhaps the best known, though the Lizard peninsula would serve as an illustration nearly as well. In the West Midlands the main road from Kidderminster to Tenbury (A.456) in passing from the Severn to the Teme valley climbs to a point some 750 feet high at Clows Top, where it crosses the road from Abberley to Cleobury Mortimer (B.4202). These two roads, and numerous smaller roads which join them, are very clearly related to the small remnant of a dissected upland-plain. They rise on to it not by way of the valleys which dissect it but by way of the intervening spurs.

Roads of this kind are often to be found in Chalk country. They occur, for instance, in the Chilterns, particularly in the area to the west of High Wycombe, in the Lincolnshire Wolds (e.g. Bluestone Heath Road, to the south and west of Louth), on Ports Down, and at many points in the North and South Downs.

On a very different type of rock a similar feature will be found in the western and north-western parts of the New Forest, and again in the Honiton area and Blackdown Hills. Some five miles west of Exeter a fine little example occurs near Whitestone, where a cluster of minor roads caps the summit of a small and highly dissected relic of an upland-surface. For modern traffic, however, the lower passage to the south of it is more convenient, and this is used by the main Exeter–Okehampton road (A.30).

In general, where the route has proved suitable for modern needs, 'skyline-roads' of this type have been incorporated in the present main-road system. Some have already been mentioned. The Guildford–Farnham road (A.31) where it passes along the Hogs Back is a well-known example. The Great North Road, in the section north of Boroughbridge, follows a low watershed within the Vale of York. Although the relief here is subdued, the outcrop of the Magnesian Limestone, on which the road is built, rises high enough to give excellent views on both sides to the Pennines and Cleveland Hills respectively. Further north, as it approaches Gateshead, the present A.1 road runs through Low Fell, along the face of an escarpment overlooking the Team valley. But it is still possible to follow the older road through Wrekenton which keeps close to the crest.

In the last case the old road, though still much used by local traffic, has been supplanted for through traffic by a road with much better gradients. In more extreme cases it is not unusual to find that old 'skyline-roads' have lost touch with modern requirements and gone out of use. The crest of the Quantock Hills, a small but clearly defined ridge rising to 1,000 feet and a little more in western Somerset, is followed along its entire length by a road. But, unlike the Cornish example discussed earlier, it is separated from the settlement of the area, which hereabouts is almost entirely confined to the surrounding lowlands. The road has not therefore been able to comply with modern requirements, and has largely passed out of use. In bolder types of country the old and the new will often be found existing together. The old road, used little or not at all by modern traffic, follows the skyline, while lower down are the newer roads or old roads which have been adapted to newer purposes. In south-west Shropshire the road from Clun to Newtown (B.4368) follows the Clun valley. Although it is an old road, many of the tracks which can still be seen on almost every ridge-top in the surrounding Clun Forest are probably older.

In the valleys of western Monmouthshire the modern roads follow the valleys where the population is concentrated in long, linear settlements. The intervening moorlands are in parts almost unpopulated, yet in nearly every case the old skyline-roads are still recognizable. And if one looks more closely still one sees that nearly all the old settlement-centres are also here on the ridge-tops. Village centres like those of Bedwellty, Mynyddislwyn, and Gelligaer contain no more than a church and a few houses. The pattern is now reversed. Industrialization has filled the once densely forested valleys with collieries, houses, and communications, but the old pattern of settlement still shows through, and the old roads which served it can still be seen as narrow by-roads or, on the higher moorlands, rough, unfenced tracks. Compare, for instance, the Roman and medieval road from Cardiff to Merthyr Tydfil along the crest of Cefn Gelligaer with its modern counterpart in the Taff valley.

The opportunities afforded by high-level routeways of this sort can be seized only by communications which are able to reach them with comparative ease. It is therefore natural that roads have made much more use of them than have other forms of transport. Canals are largely precluded from doing so by their technical properties which were discussed in Chapter I. They have the greatest difficulty in making height, they are generally less likely to find a good water-supply in such situations, and they have no incentive for climbing to reach local agricultural settlements as have some of the minor roads mentioned earlier. Occasionally one finds canals following water-partings for short distances in passing across a lowland where it is desirable as far as possible to maintain height. The Warwick & Napton Canal, for instance, follows a minor water-parting between two left-bank tributaries of the Avon as it breaks away from the Oxford Canal into the lowland of the Lias Clay near Napton. The Shropshire Union Canal between Ellesmere and Whitchurch picks its way across the North

Shropshire Plain, keeping very close to the watershed between the Severn and the Dee. But one could hardly describe these as plateau surfaces. In the Birmingham plateau, on the other hand, there is an extensive network of canals between the 400- and 500-foot contour lines (Fig. 25), but the plateau surface rises a good deal higher and the long tunnels under the main water-partings emphasize the fact that the canals are in fact closely related to the valley-systems, even though they are mostly carried along the valley-sides rather than along the valley-floors.

Occasionally one finds railways related to high-level surfaces where particular circumstances apply. A striking example is to be found in the West Riding of Yorkshire between Wakefield and Bradford. The watershed between the Aire and Calder systems rises westwards in a series of step-like features which are the small relics of earlier erosion-surfaces.[5] The skyline therefore is not level, but it is incomparably more level than any other surface between the valley-floors of the Aire in the north and the Spen–Calder in the south. Now these valley-routes were occupied by railways during the eighteen-forties, and by the end of the decade the Midland Railway had a line to Bradford up Airedale and the Lancashire & Yorkshire Railway had one up the Calder and Spen valleys. During the 'fifties there came into existence a third system which eventually formed the Great Northern Railway's approach to Bradford. The section from Wakefield to Bradford reaches the Aire–Calder watershed some two miles north-west of Wakefield and follows it closely as far as Dudley Hill in the south-eastern part of Bradford, reaching nearly 700 feet in the process. This line became a kind of spine for the Great Northern system in the West Riding. From it short lines reached out on both sides to the towns of the Aire and Calder valleys, such as Leeds, Shipley, Keighley, and Dewsbury. Nearly all the steepest gradients on the former Great Northern system (up to 1 in 50 and steeper) were to be found on these lines which link the plateau-remnant with the peripheral valleys, as for instance between Drighlington and Batley, Tingley and Batley, Laisterdyke and Bradford, Thackley and Shipley, Armley and Holbeck, the last example occurring on the direct Bradford–Leeds line which itself follows a minor watershed for much of the way.

Other examples of 'upland' railways are found on the '1,000-

[5] J. B. Sissons, 'The erosion surfaces and drainage system of South-west Yorkshire'. *Proc. Yorks. Geol. Soc.* 29 (Dec. 1954).

foot surface' in Derbyshire. 'On the Limestone this surface gives relatively easy gradients on the plateau sections of the High Peak railway and the Ashbourne–Buxton line.'[6]

One of the best examples of a railway following a high-level routeway in an area well dissected by valleys is to be found in the Holsworthy Branch of the former L.S.W.R. During the eighteen-seventies the route to Plymouth was completed through difficult country on the northern and western sides of Dartmoor. The drainage of the northern slopes of this upland runs northwards by the Taw and Torridge systems to Bideford Bay, whereas the western slopes are drained by the Tamar and Tavy systems. The Torridge and Tamar systems are separated by an important watershed which is rarely less than 500 feet above sea-level and which can be traced north-westwards from Dartmoor in a fairly straight line to within a few miles of Hartland Point, passing some two miles to the east of Holsworthy. Three and a half miles south-west of Okehampton the railway reaches this watershed just below the 1,000-foot contour line. A mile short of this summit the Holsworthy Branch, opened in 1879 and later extended to Bude,[7] diverges from the main line at Meldon Junction. Swinging north-west it immediately takes up a position on the crest of the water-shed which it follows for sixteen miles, never deviating from it by more than half a mile until it is within two miles of Holsworthy. On either side of the line the tributaries of the Torridge and Tamar have carved the plateau up into a series of valleys which lie across the path of the railway, so that any deviation from the watershed would involve the line in a number of switchbacks, if indeed it were possible to build it at all.

In all the examples so far considered it is clear that the suita-bility of a surface for carrying communications is related to the physical processes which have helped to shape it and this relation-ship springs from the fact that in nature many processes are at work which, being governed ultimately by gravitation, tend to produce horizontal surfaces. There is no agent of erosion which illustrates this better than the sea. The sea is capable of two main processes; it can cut away a pre-existing land-surface and it can transport and deposit material to build up new landforms. The processes are clearly related, since the material used in building

---

[6] K. M. Clayton, 'The geomorphology of the area around Nottingham and Derby'. *E. Mids. Geog.* No. 3 (June 1955), p. 16.

[7] B. G. Wilson, 'The North Cornwall Line of the Southern Region'. *Rly. Mag.* 95 (Sept.–Oct. 1949), p. 326.

up beaches is often derived largely, though not entirely, from the onslaught made by wave action on marine cliffs. Very often the resultant landform is the product of both processes, as when a beach is formed on a wave-cut platform of solid rock. In consequence one might expect to find that landforms which are the product of marine action are peculiarly well suited to the requirements of communications in providing a level path, and in some cases this is so.

The surfaces produced by marine action do not merely comprise the beaches and wave-cut platforms at present being built and maintained by the sea. Owing to changes of sea-level one often finds such surfaces at quite high elevations. Some of those already referred to as plateau surfaces or upland-plains are of marine origin, such as, for instance, the surface related to the early Pleistocene marine transgression in Wiltshire, and there is no need to discuss them further. Neither is it necessary here to enter the arena of argument about the precise origin and dating of these surfaces. Anyone who wishes to savour the controversy which surrounds them, particularly in the matter of dating, may refer to Steers' work on the coasts.[8] But some attention must be given to the 'raised beaches' which are encountered at many points round the coasts of Britain and which, in some areas, are of the greatest importance for communications.

The most striking examples come from Scotland where raised beaches are found not only on the coasts themselves but also flanking many of the firths or arms of the sea, particularly in the north-east. The use which settlement has made of these features was pointed out by Miss Meiklejohn,[9] who also noted that the road and railway follow them for many miles. In no section of the coast is this more clearly emphasized than in the twenty-five miles between Dornoch Firth and Helmsdale. Practically the whole of this coast is fringed by raised beaches which are designated on the geological map[10] as '15 foot', '25 foot', and '100 foot'. Sometimes these raised beaches are separated from the present beach by dunes of blown sand which in places have spread out over the raised beaches themselves as at the entrance to Loch Fleet (Fig. 8).

Between Dornoch and Loch Fleet the present main road passes

[8] J. A. Steers, *The Coastline of England and Wales* (1946); *The Sea Coast* (The New Naturalist) (1954).
[9] G. Meiklejohn, *The Settlements and Roads of Scotland* (1927).
[10] O.S. 1-inch Geological Map, sheet 103.

G.C.—F

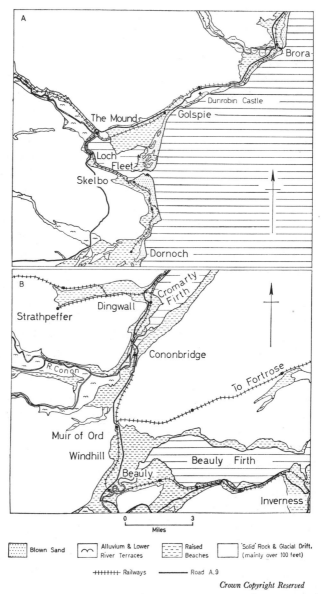

FIG. 8. COMMUNICATIONS AND RAISED BEACHES IN NORTH-EAST SCOTLAND

A. The coastline between Dornoch and Brora, Sutherland.
B. Raised beaches at the heads of the Cromarty and Beauly Firths.

over the upland of Old Red Sandstone in a fairly straight line, but the railway (the Dornoch branch of the former Highland Railway) follows the 25-foot and 50-foot raised beaches for the whole of its course (between Dornoch and the Mound), except where it strays on to the blown sand near Skelbo Station and where it crosses the Fleet River by an artificial embankment. Beyond (i.e. north-east of) the Mound, the influence exerted by these raised beaches is even more apparent. Once round the Old Red Sandstone bluff which stretches right up to the Fleet estuary, the railway passes on to the 25-foot raised beach which it follows to Golspie. Further on, near Brora, the 50-foot and 100-foot beaches are used. There is another stretch of raised beach over half a mile wide near Loth Station, which narrows down to a thin strip sometimes only a few yards wide as Helmsdale is approached. It forms a tiny shelf cut into the steep slopes which sweep down from Creag Loisgte into the sea..There is only one place in the whole of this section where the railway does not keep to the raised beaches or, locally, the sand dunes, and that is at Dunrobin Castle, the seat of the Dukes of Sutherland. This is not due to any interruption in the raised beaches at this point, but to the fact that the grounds of the castle, which is built overlooking the 25-foot beach, come right down to the sea. Now when the Sutherland Railway was opened in 1868, it reached only as far as Golspie,[11] and the building of the line from there to Helmsdale was undertaken by the Duke himself, who very understandably preferred to take it behind (that is to the north of) the castle, even though this meant forsaking the raised beaches for the drift-covered slopes of the Jurassic rocks and raising the line on a gradient of 1 in 60 at each side to a summit-level of 188 feet. It would appear that this part of the line was the most difficult to construct, since the two-mile section from Golspie to Dunrobin took eight months longer to complete than the fifteen miles from there to the edge of Helmsdale, and the engine and coaches used for working the line had to be taken across the gap by road.[12]

Although it takes more liberties with the landscape Telford's road, the present A.9, follows the railway (and therefore the raised beaches) fairly closely for a dozen miles or so. It also makes the deviation behind Dunrobin. But from Helmsdale onwards towards Wick the situation is very different. The raised beaches only occur intermittently. They are not sufficiently continuous to

[11] H. A. Vallance, *The History of the Highland Railway* (1938), p. 36.
[12] ibid., p. 38.

provide a line of communication at all, and road and railway are therefore obliged to find another passage. The road continues north-east, rising on to the Ord of Caithness and then pursuing a switchback course over the moorlands and into the steep little valleys which have dissected it as they flow separately to the sea. The railway, on the other hand, is forced inland up the valley of the Helmsdale River (Strath Ullie) to find a totally different kind of approach this north-eastern extremity of the British mainland. The contrast in the pattern of communications on either side of Helmsdale can be very largely explained in terms of its raised beaches.

One other example from north-east Scotland is worth considering briefly. It concerns the communications between Inverness and Cromarty Firth (Fig. 8). Road and railway both leave Inverness on a narrow strip of raised beach which flanks the southern shore of Beauly Firth and opens out into a broad expanse at the head of the firth. As it crosses the River Beauly the railway sweeps northward round the village of Beauly keeping rigidly to the raised beaches all the way. To the north of Beauly for two miles and more the beaches form a series of steps reaching a height of a little over 100 feet at Muir of Ord. Near Windhill road and railway can be seen climbing up from one beach to another making for the gap in the low hills at Muir of Ord which leads through to the Conon valley. The lower part of this valley, as it opens out to form the head of Cromarty Firth, is flanked on both sides by well-defined raised beaches. At Cononbridge both road and rail swing sharply across the alluvium of the valley striking directly on to the raised beaches on the other side which they both follow to Dingwall.

Among other examples of raised beaches being used for communications may be mentioned those which fringe the coast just to the north of Ayr. At Kilwinning the railways coming south-west from Glasgow divide. The lines to Ardrossan and Saltcoats turn west; the line to Troon keeps on to the south. In neither case would it be an exaggeration to say that the path followed by the lines is mainly determined by the levels of the raised beaches. From Workington to Maryport (Cumberland) both the road (A.596) and railway follow a raised beach, and beyond Maryport the Silloth road (B.5300) returns to the raised beach at Bank End and then follows it all the way, while among the canals the Forth and Clyde follows the 100-foot beach at its eastern end.[13]

[13] A. G. Ogilvie, *Great Britain: Essays in Regional Geography* (1937), p. 452.

Where cliffs form the coastline the position of the communications is likely to depend very much on the nature of the land-surface which is being attacked by the sea. Sometimes this may be a well-developed plateau surface, in which case the communications linking the coastal settlements may be based on it. The string of small coastal settlements between Buckie and Cullen

Photo: Aerofilms

PLATE 12. CULLEN, BANFFSHIRE

The former Great North of Scotland Railway links up the fishing ports of the Banffshire coast, the rocky nature of which clearly precludes the possibility of a cliff-base railway. The line therefore keeps to the upland surface, even though this is severely interrupted by the ravines of youthful rivers. Note the absence of any rail connexion with the harbour. View to the east.

(Banffshire) are served by a railway of this sort (Plate 12). Between Cromer and Mundesley (Norfolk) road and railway keep to the surface above the cliffs. Between Rottingdean and Newhaven (Sussex) the coast road, A.259, follows the chalk upland through Peacehaven. North of Berwick the East Coast main line makes its way to Burnmouth along the slopes which continue rising above the cliff-top, and the Great North Road lies parallel with it a little further up.

Sometimes, however, the surface into which the cliff is being worn back may be less suitable for carrying roads or railways, or there may be some particular reason why they should keep as near sea-level as possible, as for instance in resorts. The main road through St. Leonards and Hastings (A.259) is an example; the Marine Drive at Scarborough is another. These roads are carried along the cliff-base not because there is no possible alternative

Photo: Aerofilms

PLATE 13. THE PARSON AND CLERK, DEVON

The main line from Paddington to Plymouth accepts the less difficult alternative in keeping to the base rather than the top of the cliff in its passage from Dawlish to Teignmouth (behind the camera). Note the undulating surface of the land which can be crossed by the road but not the railway. View to the north-east.

means of passing through, but because of the particular facilities which such a road aims to provide. But sometimes a cliff-base route is chosen because it is less difficult than a cliff-top route. Probably the best known example is between Dawlish and Teignmouth (Devon), where the main line of railway from Paddington to Plymouth has to pass from the estuary of the Exe to that of the Teign. Both estuaries have convenient stretches of level land flanking the water but between the two is a difficult piece of country rising to some 800 feet and heavily dissected by many small streams. Between the mouths of the Exe and Teign lies a stretch of rocky cliff scenery some four miles long, and when the railway came to be built the only practicable course lay at the base of the cliff (Plate 13). A good deal of constructional work was necessary. A sea-wall had to be built up from the beach and the irregularity of the cliff-line made it impossible for the railway to

Photo: Aerofilms

PLATE 14. PENMAEN-MAWR, CAERNARVONSHIRE

The North Wales coast road (A.55) and the London–Holyhead railway both follow the strip of coastal plain which is interrupted at Penmaen-mawr by this projecting bastion of the Snowdon *massif*. Both manage to overcome the obstacle with the aid of short tunnels. The task is not made any easier by the extensive quarrying. View to the east.

follow it precisely, so that tunnelling was necessary where the rocks projected into the sea, as at the Parson and Clerk. Even so it is apparent that the levelling operations of the sea provided the essential physical basis for this piece of railway.

Other examples of cliff-base railways may be found in Cumberland between Workington and Whitehaven, and in Caernarvonshire at Penmaen-bach and Penmaen-mawr (Plate 14). The line between Folkestone and Dover approaches the shoreline at the Dover end, but rises continuously westwards up the cliff face and at Folkestone is well above sea-level. It was originally built on wooden trestles placed on the foreshore at the cliff-base.[14] To the north and south of Barmouth (Merioneth) there occur examples of cliff-base railways at Llwyngwril and Llanaber respectively. At the latter place there has been much difficulty in maintaining the sea-wall on which the track is laid.[15]

Sometimes, however, there is no easy routeway along a cliff-line either at the base or at the top. A receding cliff cuts indiscriminately into a surface which may be level (as in the Banffshire examples) or may not. It may then be quite impracticable to carry a line of communication along the coast at all and it will be forced inland. Such a situation arises in west Dorset and east Devon. The drainage here consists of numerous small streams running independently to the coast. The cliffs, therefore, as seen from the sea, have a corrugated effect, rising to 500 feet and more, then plunging to sea-level where the streams run out. This is clearly an unsuitable surface for a railway and even for a road, and since there is no adequate passage at the cliff-base, both are forced inland. Here the tributary valleys of the larger streams, such as the Otter and the Axe, enable the railway to find a reasonable though hilly route between Salisbury and Exeter. The small seaside towns of Sidmouth, Seaton, Lyme Regis, Bridport-West Bay, and Abbotsbury are, or were, connected to the inland lines by short terminal branches. The roads, on the other hand, make free use of the intervening upland-surfaces. Looking at it on the map one obtains an impression of the coast as an irregular line cutting arbitrarily into a nicely adjusted pattern of road, railway, hill, and valley. Coastal landforms, therefore, are not always positive aids to the building of communications.

Spits, bars, and other shorelines of accretion seem at first sight to offer certain advantages, being level and often straight. Yet in the great majority of cases they are not used by roads or railways. This is often due to their situation, particularly in the case of spits, such as those of Orford Ness and Blakeney point which lead virtually nowhere and have no advantages for any kind of economic development though they may have some strategic significance. At Spurn Head (Yorkshire) the local requirements of the lighthouse, lifeboat, coastguard station, and various

---

[14] The structure is illustrated in a print displayed in the Science Museum, South Kensington.

[15] 'Coast defence works near Barmouth' (Editorial article). *Rly. Mag.* cii (March 1956), p. 185.

military installations have together been responsible for the provision of both a railway and a road, ʹof which only the latter survives.

In a different situation a spit may acquire importance by narrowing down the width of a water-body and making it easier to cross by bridge or ferry. Thus the entrance to Poole Harbour (Dorset) is narrowed to about a quarter of a mile by converging spits which carry the Bournemouth–Swanage road as it approaches the Sandbanks Ferry. The ferry across Langstone Harbour (Hampshire) gave rise to similar road-approaches on the spits. At Blyth (Northumberland) the harbour is enclosed on its eastern side by Cambois Links 'which form a long spit running to the south-east and continued into reefs covered at high water. The river Blyth is thus deflected to the south. . . .'[16] It is this deflected mouth of the river which forms the harbour of Blyth, and although the town is situated on the inland or south-western side, and although the main communications approach from this side, the railway from a group of collieries to the north-west runs down the spit to give independent access to the staithes on the north-eastern side of the harbour. In Great Yarmouth, where a very similar feature occurs, the town centre itself is on the spit.

In exceptional cases, as at Slapton Ley (Devon), shingle bars may be used to carry a coast road, and at Chesil the narrow neck of land, by which road and railway link the Isle of Portland with the mainland, is none other than the end of the famous beach. Generally, however, these coastal landforms are not particularly well suited to the development of communications.

Sand dunes are particularly unsatisfactory. They are often too poorly consolidated to form a firm bed, they may be anything but level, and until properly clothed with vegetation they are in danger of moving.

On the shores of the Moray Firth, part of the Burghead & Hopeman Railway was destroyed by moving sand[17] and in South Wales, at the mouths of the Kenfig and Ogmore rivers, roads were overwhelmed in the fifteenth and sixteenth centuries respectively.[18] In the same area the course followed by the railway is instructive. MacDermot records that, after the passage of the South Wales Railway Act of 1845, two 'extensive deviations' were applied for,

---

[16] J. A. Steers, op. cit. (1946), p. 458.
[17] A. C. O'Dell, 'A geographical examination of the development of Scottish railways'. *S.G.M.* 55 (1939), p. 136.
[18] J. A. Steers, op. cit. (1946), pp. 178–9.

one between Carmarthen and Kidwelly to carry the line by the coast
and so improve the gradients and lessen the earthwork, which would
have included a tunnel, at the expense of an additional three miles;
the other between Aberavon and Bridgend with exactly the opposite
effect, to avoid the coast and the shifting sands of Newton Nottage and
pass inland by Pyle and Margam, three miles shorter but with worse
gradients.[19]

Now in the former case the railway as originally authorized would
have followed the lower part of the valley of the Gwendraeth

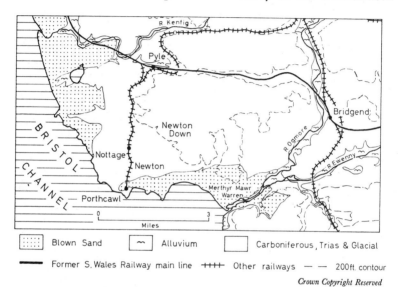

FIG. 9. RAILWAYS NEAR BRIDGEND, GLAMORGAN

Fach up from Kidwelly, and would then have had to pass over
(or in view of the tunnel perhaps one should say under) the inter-
fluve between the valleys of the Gwendraeth Fach and Towy. The
deviation secured for the railway a level course over alluvium,
boulder-clay, and in places the marls of Old Red Sandstone age
with comparatively little interference from the small patches of
blown sand which intermittently fringe the estuaries. On the other
hand the Aberavon–Bridgend deviation (Fig. 9) enabled the line
to avoid the much more formidable spread of sand dunes already
mentioned. If, as was originally planned, the railway had followed
the Ogmore valley below Bridgend far enough to outflank the
300-foot Carboniferous Limestone plateau of Newton Down, it

---

[19] E. T. MacDermot, *History of the Great Western Railway*, 1 (1927), p. 559.

would have found itself well within the sands of Merthyr Mawr Warren, since these sands have been carried right up the face of the Carboniferous Limestone, and there is therefore no surface between it and the sea on this southern side which is not composed of sand dunes. The villages of Newton and Nottage and the town of Porthcawl have grown up on a projection of Carboniferous and Triassic rocks flanked on both sides by sand-dune coasts which are still devoid of communications. Both the road (A.4106) and the railway to Porthcawl approach it from inland, keeping to the outcrops of solid rock.

In South Wales comparatively little has been done to fix the dunes and they are still in most cases partially free to move under the influence of the wind. In some areas, however, dunes have undergone various kinds of modification which render them less unsatisfactory for communications. The coast of south Lancashire between Southport and Liverpool is a case in point. The geological map[20] shows a spread of blown sand which at Formby reaches a width of nearly three miles, and by 1750 streets in Formby were becoming buried.[21] But the Land Utilization Survey Map[22] shows that, in contrast to the South Wales dunes, the greater part of the blown sand in 1931-2 was under some form of land use other than 'Heathland, Moorland, Commons and rough pasture', with all the other five categories of land use represented. Although the Liverpool–Southport line of the former L. & Y. Railway rests on blown sand nearly all the way from Waterloo (Liverpool) to Southport, much of the surface is of a very different type from that of Kenfig Burrows or Merthyr Mawr Warren. Where the natural dunes are best developed, immediately behind the shoreline, the communications are confined to a few access roads to the beach. Only in the immediate approaches to Southport does the former C.L.C. railway swing into the dune-belt proper[23] (Plate 15).

Estuaries have a very influential role to play in the geography of communications, but it would be dangerous to embark on generalizations without first making it clear that the term covers a very wide range of morphological types. At one end of the scale are the tidal mouths of rivers like the Tyne or Wear which hardly funnel out at all as they approach the sea. At the other end are the branching systems of drowned valleys or rias, like Carrick Roads

[20] O.S. 1-inch Geological Map, sheet 89.
[21] J. A. Steers, op. cit. (1946), p. 101.   [22] L.U.S. 1-inch map, sheet 35.
[23] For morphological details see R. K. Gresswell, *Sandy Shores in South Lancashire* (1953).

Crown Copyright Reserved—Royal Air Force Photograph

PLATE 15. RAILWAYS AT AINSDALE, LANCASHIRE

The former Lancashire & Yorkshire line from Liverpool to Southport runs approximately along the line of junction between the dunes and the improved land. The abandoned line of the Cheshire Lines Committee enters the dune-belt and follows it into Southport (Lord Street). Apart from this the dune-belt proper is devoid of communications. View to the south-east.

and the Hamoaze. The fjords of western Scotland, being submerged glaciated valleys, also properly come in this category but are in many ways quite distinctive.

The effect of estuaries on communications is partly positive but mainly negative. They interpose barriers which have to be crossed or avoided. The efficacy of these barriers is only partly governed by the size of the river concerned. Rivers of moderate and even large size by British standards may be bridged quite near their mouths. The Wear at Sunderland, the Tweed at Berwick, the Dee and Don at Aberdeen are examples. In these cases there is scarcely any development of the estuaries. Sometimes estuaries which are too wide to be bridged in the widest part narrow some-

Photo: Aerofilms

PLATE 16. RUNCORN GAP

Much of the Mersey estuary is flanked by a belt of alluvium, but at this point the firm ground of drift-covered Trias closes in and both road and railway cross at the narrow passage. The advantage of the transporter bridge is that it can convey road traffic on a suspended platform at low level and yet secure adequate clearance for shipping. Its disadvantages do not require comment. It is being replaced by a new high-level road bridge. Note how both bridges also span the Manchester Ship Canal, which is protected by a narrow bank against changes of water-level in the tidal Mersey. If necessary, however, entrance or exit can be made at Runcorn by the lock, seen beyond the transporter bridge. View to the east-north-east.

what towards their mouths. This happens in Loch Etive (Argyll) at Connel Ferry and in the Mawddach estuary (Merioneth) at Barmouth. The two great railway bridges of eastern Scotland are situated where the estuaries of the Forth and Tay become narrower than further upstream, and the bridges at Runcorn are at a similar constriction in the Mersey (Plate 16). The Humber Bridge, if it is ever built, is likely to be in a similar situation. The configuration of the estuary-bed may also play an important part. The Firth of Tay, for instance, is shallow enough to permit the construction of

PLATE 17. THE TAY BRIDGE

The large number and close spacing of the piers reflects the shallow nature of the firth. Note how the bridge is curved to bring the line into the centre of Dundee (the western part of which can be seen) parallel with the Tay waterfront. In order to pass through the centre of the city, the line has to be carried under the street at the dock side, and is at about the same level as the water in the firth. The track therefore has to rise sharply (1 in 114) in order to obtain the necessary clearance over the deep channel. From the central section southwards it continues to rise but at a more gentle gradient (1 in 762). At the southern end of the bridge (foreground) the line forks for Tayport (right) and for Leuchars and the Forth Bridge (left). View to the north-west.

a line of piers all the way across the river (Plate 17). In the Firth of Forth, which is much deeper, this method would be impracticable and a totally different type of bridge has had to be built, with its three piers and massive cantilevers (Plate 18).

The efficacy of any barrier of this sort depends not only on its physical development but also on the economic necessity for crossing it. The geographical situation of estuaries is particularly significant in this respect. Many of the lochs of western Scotland would be easier to bridge than, say, the Firth of Forth, but the lack of potential traffic would make such an event most unlikely. The economic aspect is clearly fundamental and the big road-bridging

Photo: Aerofilms

PLATE 18. THE FORTH BRIDGES

The central cantilever of the railway bridge can be seen resting on the rock of Inch Garvie in the middle of the firth. The suspension bridge which will carry the road is under construction further upstream (foreground). Between the two can be seen the vehicular ferry and pier at North Queensferry. View to the south-east.

schemes at present being considered and carried out are allotted priority on this basis. Until quite recently, however, the money available for this kind of project has been in the hands of the railway companies rather than the highway authorities, and, as commercial undertakings, the railways have found it worthwhile to invest capital on a scale which the differently constituted road authorities could not afford. Consequently it is usual to find in large estuaries that the lowest bridge is a railway bridge. The Forth, Tay, Tamar, and Severn, are all crossed by railways many miles below the lowest road bridge. At one time the same applied to the Solway. Even on smaller estuaries, such as those on the north of Morecambe Bay, the lowest road bridges are much higher than those of the railway. Where road and rail cross together it may be a matter of accident which is the lower. On the Tyne it is the road, on the Clyde the railway, but only by a few feet. Sometimes road and rail are carried across by the same structure as at Connel Ferry (Argyll), Keadby (Lincolnshire), and the Traeth Bach (Merioneth). To what extent the programme of modern road construction is changing this situation is a question which will be further discussed in Chapter IX.

In addition to the influence they exert as barriers to communications, estuaries often provide opportunities for lines of penetration from the coast inland. Several small ports, such as Harwich, Fowey, and Looe (Fig. 7), which owe their origin to estuaries, are connected inland by railways which follow their shores. Several examples of such railways have already been mentioned as in the Tovy, Teign, and Exe valleys. O'Dell cites the West Highland line along Loch Eil which 'avoids gradients by clinging to the shore under the lee of the sea-walls'.[24] Sometimes, however, where branching systems are well developed, the continuity of the shores is broken by creeks, and railways may have to pass from one section of an estuary shore to another, by bridges. An example may be found in the estuary of the Camel (Padstow line, Cornwall) or on the approaches of the former Southern Railway line to Plymouth as it follows the eastern shores of the Tamar estuary. At Dartmouth, Devon, the shores of the estuary on the western side are considerably interrupted in this way. The railway, however, approaching from Tor Bay, is able to find a comparatively easy passage along the eastern side of Dartmouth Harbour to its terminus at Kingswear, immediately opposite to the historic little port which still has to be reached from the railway station by ferry (Plate 19).

In areas of more gentle relief, roads are not usually so strongly attracted to the estuaries as railways. Hardly anywhere are the numerous estuaries of the Essex coast flanked by roads. But bolder relief tends to force the roads also towards the estuaries. In central Wales the Mawddach and Dyfi estuaries are both flanked by roads as well as railways, and in the fjord coasts of western Scotland the few roads which reach the coast at all generally do so by following the fjord sides. Loch Broom, Loch Duich, Loch Sunart, and Loch Leven are examples. Much of the shore of Loch Fyne is flanked by roads, while Loch Carron (Wester Ross) has a road on one side and a railway on the other.

Perhaps the best example in Britain of an estuary of the ria type

[24] A. C. O'Dell, op. cit., p. 137.

Photo: Aerofilms

PLATE 19. KINGSWEAR, DEVON

The side of the ria of Dartmouth Harbour forms the approach-route of the railway. The creek (right) which is typical of these estuaries, is too small to interfere seriously with the passage of the line. Note the juxtaposition of the terminal station and the ferry-pier. Most of the traffic arriving here is destined for Dartmouth on the other side of the estuary. View towards the north-east.

is Milford Haven. This many-branching inlet is reached by railways at three terminal points, Pembroke Dock on the south, Milford Haven and Neyland on the north. These railways all approach the estuary by inland routes, though in the last two cases the final approach to the termini is along the shores of small creeks. The main reaches of the estuary are sharply if not deeply incised into a low plateau surface, and the railways have been prevented from making use of their shorelines by their extreme irregularity.

Sometimes the crossing of estuaries was achieved in association with schemes for land reclamation, a common embankment serving both purposes. The embankment at Portmadoc was primarily intended to bring about the reclamation of the Traeth Mawr, the sandy estuary of the Afon Glaslyn, but it has also been used to carry the main road and the narrow-gauge Ffestiniog

G.C.—G

Railway. (The main line of the former Cambrian Railway uses another embankment further inland to cross the river and reclaimed flats.) The Mound (Fig. 8) was primarily intended to provide a crossing of the Fleet estuary, but was also expected to yield new farming land from the waters of the firth. Schemes for similar dual purpose embankments were more than once put forward in connexion with the crossing of the estuaries of Furness.[25]

The main erosional features of glaciation have been considered in an earlier chapter. There are, however, other landforms which are the result of deposition associated with glaciation. In Britain these are rarely very large and they play a much smaller part in the geography of communications than, say, in Finland, Denmark, or even Eire. But some of the better-developed moraines have exerted an influence on local road-patterns, especially where they occur in low-lying country, in which they give rise to higher and firmer ground. In the Vale of York, for instance, the Escrick Moraine is followed for much of its length by an old road. Further east the ridges of drift which rise out of the alluvial and lacustrine flats of Holderness are intimately related to the old road-pattern.

Reference has already been made to landforms, such as sand dunes, whose instability poses difficulties for the building of communications. It will be appropriate to conclude this brief review of miscellaneous landforms with a reference to some other types of surface which are in one way or another unstable. In former times one would have been justified in including in this category the clay-belts which outcrop notably among the Mesozoic rocks of Lowland Britain. Here the instability applied only to the immediate surface, but under the primitive techniques of road-making which sometimes involved little more than the designation of a right of way over a natural or little improved clay surface, this was enough to make roads on such outcrops in summer rough and treacherous, in winter impassable. The accounts of travellers of the seventeenth and eighteenth centuries leave no doubt as to the condition of such roads, and the worst vituperations of such writers as Arthur Young, which make good reading, are reserved for the clay-lands.[26]

---

[25] J. D. Marshall, *Furness and the Industrial Revolution* (1958), Chapter IX.

[26] See H. C. Darby, *An Historical Geography of England before 1800*, in which three contributors, E. G. R. Taylor, J. N. L. Baker, and W. G. East all stress the significance of the clay-lands in this connexion. E. G. R. Taylor (p. 341) cites several examples of causeways mentioned by Leland in such situations. See also J. B. Mitchell, *Historical Geography* (1954), pp. 301 et seq.

To modern communications clay surfaces of this kind present no obstacle, but peat surfaces are much less stable and have proved more difficult to cross, particularly where railways are concerned. Even before the railway era, road engineers like Metcalf had used brushwood for making a foundation on marshy surfaces, and this method was used also by railway engineers. One of the earliest railways to encounter a problem of this sort was the Liverpool & Manchester (1825–30) which was carried across the well-known Chat Moss. A little later the Great Northern main line (1846–50) was built and this had to pass over a section of the Fens near Holme. Grinling's account of the technique used is as follows:

Then he [Stephen Ballard] had a number of rafts built of alternative layers of faggots and peat sods, and, having laid these on the swampy ground, he added weight to them little by little, so that the water was gradually forced out, while what solid matter there was beneath them was not displaced. In this way a comparatively firm foundation was secured, and on this was built not only the embankment of the line, but the brickwork for the bridges also, the same principle being observed in this work as in the other, namely, that the weight should be added very gradually so as to give plenty of time for the water to find its way out.[27]

Today the track is capable of carrying fast and heavy loads, speeds of 90 m.p.h. and over having been recorded here. Even so there would seem to be a slow sinking. Darby,[28] quoting an official railway source, says:

The normal annual subsidence along a railway track due to the 'draw' associated with the sinking of the fen is about $\frac{1}{2}$ to 1 inch. But in abnormally dry weather the gradual subsidence of a comparatively high embankment may be as much as 7 inches (1934–35). . . . In many cases culverts cannot function properly because they have been placed on piles, and so have not sunk with the adjoining lands and ditches.

Landslips, screes, and similar unstable landforms are generally local phenomena and do not necessarily preclude, though they may complicate, the building of communications. For instance at Ventnor (I.O.W.) and Folkstone Warren roads and railway respectively rest on material which has slipped. In the latter place, ever since the opening in 1844, great trouble has been caused by further movement of the Chalk resting on the impermeable Gault.[29]

[27] C. H. Grinling, *The History of the Great Northern Railway* (1898), p. 81.
[28] H. C. Darby, *The Draining of the Fens* (2nd ed. 1956), p. 229, footnote.
[29] F. H. Edmunds, *British Regional Geology. The Wealden District.* (3rd ed. 1954), pp. vi and 63 and Plate X B.

During the First World War a movement occurred which resulted in the line being closed for over three and a half years, and recently expensive steps have had to be taken to drain the Chalk behind the landslip and at the same time to prevent erosion of the 'toe' by the provision of a modern type of sea-wall.[30]

On the Derby–Manchester line trouble was encountered at Buxworth (or Bugsworth) soon after its completion in 1866.[31] As the line from Chapel-en-le-Frith enters the Goyt valley it sweeps round the slopes of a hill called Chinley Churn. This hillside was not firm enough to support a viaduct, and the line had to be reconstructed on a new alignment for some 300 yards, while extensive drainage operations were carried out in the shales.

In these examples landslipping has caused instability of the surface on which the railways are built. It can also give rise to the deposition of material from valley-sides across roads and railways. Both consequences of instability, inadequacy of foundations and liability to falls of debris, may occur in the same place; a good example can be seen in the Cliviger Gorge.[32]

A common cause of trouble arises from excavations connected with the actual processes of railway construction, such as in tunnels and cuttings which may encounter unstable rock. The cutting on the former Midland line just north of Sheffield Station is an example. Here the stability of the Coal Measures sandstones had been destroyed by mining and quarrying operations. 'We dared not tunnel. The only course left was to make an open cutting for about half a mile, with an immense number of bridges. . . .' So the engineer is reputed to have described it,[33] and the bridges can certainly still be seen. In such cases the shape of a cutting will often give an indication of the stability of the rock in which it is cut. In hard rock vertical sides may be left bare, whereas in a softer material it will be necessary either to widen out the cutting-section so that the angle of the sides will approximate to the angle of repose of the material, or alternatively to hold up the sides at a steeper angle by retaining walls. In some cases cross-bracing may be necessary, as at Roade (Northants). A good opportunity to compare cutting sections occurs near Durham. At Croxdale, to the south of the city, the main line passes through

---

[30] 'Coast erosion works in Folkestone Warren'. *Rly. Mag.* c (Sept. 1954), pp. 601–4.
[31] F. S. Williams, *The Midland Railway* (1877), pp. 420–2.
[32] I. A. Williamson, 'A Guide to the geology of the Cliviger Valley, near Burnley, Lancashire'. *Proc. Yorks. Geol. Soc.* 30 (1956), pp. 402–3.
[33] F. S. Williams, op. cit., p. 446.

Coal Measures sandstones in a vertical-walled cutting of bare rock. At Neville's Cross, some four miles further north, a deeper cutting carries it through a hill of boulder-clay. At the bottom the sides are maintained in a near-vertical plane by retaining walls some 10 feet high at the top of which the cutting splays out in a wide V-shaped cross-section. Most sandstones and limestones, including,

Photo: Brian Fisher

PLATE 20. RAILWAY CUTTING NEAR LITTLE WEIGHTON, YORKSHIRE

This cutting carries the former Hull & Barnsley Railway through the Chalk in the course of its passage across the Yorkshire Wolds. It has not been necessary to line the cutting with retaining walls, but the large quantity of material which has accumulated in the cutting clearly indicates that the steepness of the sides is near its maximum. View to the north-west.

in places the Chalk, are capable of maintaining vertical or near-vertical sides in cuttings (Plate 20). Clays and poorly consolidated sands are not. The distinction may be important in towns where land-values are high and the extra land needed for a V-section cutting makes it an expensive investment. Most of the shallow railways of the London Underground system, for instance, are built in cuttings with brick retaining walls to maintain vertical sides and thereby save valuable land.

Finally this is perhaps the appropriate place to mention one other kind of unstable surface although its instability is man-made. This is mining subsidence. In most colliery areas it is possible to find notices giving warning of roads subject to subsidence. Many stretches of railway are also designated as 'subject to temporary speed restrictions' on this account, for instance in the Derbyshire Coalfield from Stanton Gate to Clay Cross (former Midland main line), in the South Lancashire Coalfield from Rainford to Pendleton (former L. & Y. line between Liverpool and Manchester), in the Lanarkshire Coalfield on the main line through Motherwell, and in the Wrexham Coalfield on the Shrewsbury–Chester line.[34] Where subsidence has been serious over a long period it is often necessary to raise the track so as to maintain the gradients. Station platforms must be raised to an equivalent level, whereas the station buildings are allowed to sink with the land-surface. There are some particularly good examples on the Newcastle–Hexham line, but the phenomenon can be seen easily enough in most coalfields. In the nineteen-thirties mining subsidence made Polesworth notorious for speed restrictions on the West Coast main line.

Some of the most serious subsidence has occurred in the Cheshire salt-fields, and special steps have been necessary to deal with it. The Elton Viaduct on the Manchester–Crewe line presented such a problem that it has had to be replaced by a so-called 'Tubercular bridge'[35] consisting of a 'cellular' structure of concrete pipes to which further tiers can be added as further subsidence takes place.

The communications most susceptible to subsidence are the canals, since for obvious reasons it is imperative to maintain the levels, and this involves the building-up of the banks often by many feet. One of the most impressive yardsticks by which subsidence can be measured is to be seen at Etruria in the North Stafford-shire coalfield. Here Josiah Wedgwood built his factory in 1769 on the Trent & Mersey Canal. The factory can still be seen, but the canal today is level with the first-floor windows (Plate 21). The traffic on this waterway has justified the expense of building up the banks as the land-surface subsides. In the southern outskirts of Wigan the Wigan & Leigh Canal passes through the 'flashes' (areas flooded as a result of mining subsidence), being confined by parallel embankments which have been built up to maintain it at

[34] *Gradients of the British Main Line Railways.* The Railway Publishing Co. (1936).
[35] *The Times*, 15 Feb. 1958.

a higher level than the surrounding water.[36] The final consequences can be seen on the Dearne & Dove Canal in south Yorkshire, which 'has been severely affected by mining subsidence and
is unnavigable for most of its length'.[37] Where, at the place of
subsidence, the canal is in tunnel, remedial measures may be
almost impossible, since any rise in the water-level relative to the

Photo: S. H. Beaver

PLATE 21. ETRURIA WORKS, STAFFORDSHIRE

Wedgwood's works of 1769 on the banks of the Trent & Mersey Canal, with
part of the Shelton Iron and Steel Works in the distance. All the buildings have
subsided with the land-surface, but the canal has of necessity been maintained
at its original level. View to the north-west.

tunnel will diminish the headroom. Several tunnels have been
closed owing to mining subsidence, among them the Lappal
(Birmingham), Norwood (Chesterfield), and Butterley (Cromford), all over 3,000 yards in length.[38]

[36] Roy Millward, *Lancashire* (*The Making of the English Landscape*) (1955), pp. 18–20.
[37] *Canals & Inland Waterways. Report of the Board of Survey* (1955), p. 17.
[38] L. A. Edwards, *Inland Waterways of Great Britain and Northern Ireland* (1950),
pp. 412–13.

CHAPTER IV

STRUCTURE, DRAINAGE, AND COMMUNICATIONS

The discussion so far has concerned the way in which different kinds of communications have been fitted on to the surface of landforms of various shapes, and it has been shown that some properties of these landforms make it comparatively easy to build lines of communication while others make it difficult. At the heart of this relationship lies the question of differences in altitude. Stability of the surface and the opportunity to develop straight lines in a horizontal plane are important, but it is generally the vertical rise and fall of the ground which emerges as the dominant influence controlling the development of a pattern of communications.

This balance between upland and lowland is usually reflected in the drainage-systems. But the rivers of these drainage-systems may themselves be excavating a landscape, the main features of which are determined by the structure of the underlying rocks. The occurrence of lowlands may then bear a more direct relationship to the outcrops of easily eroded rocks than to the limits of the present drainage-system, according to certain principles which cannot be elaborated here but which are made clear in any good geomorphological textbook.

For example, if one travels from Swindon to Cirencester along the A.419 road, shortly after joining the line of the Roman road one descends Blunsdon Hill and follows an expanse of low-lying land through Cricklade before rising again on approaching Cirencester. It would be correct to describe this low-lying land as the valley of the Upper Thames (or Isis), but equally correct to call it the Oxford Clay Vale. The river has excavated a broad valley, the general direction of which has been largely controlled by the outcrop of the Oxford Clay. Similarly we could say that at Blunsdon Hill A.419 descends the southern flank of the Isis valley or that it descends the face of the Corallian escarpment.

Where, as in this case, the land-surface has been developed on a series of inclined strata, those rocks which are most resistant to weathering tend to stand out in escarpments and to become identified with the watersheds between the river-systems. In some other districts, East Anglia, for instance, where the river-systems are scarcely less clearly developed, it is not possible to identify valleys with particular geological outcrops in the same way, since the structure is quite different. But it should be clear from the foregoing that, if one is to consider some of the ways in which communications are related, not merely to valley-sections or to plateau surfaces, but to alternations of contrasting types of landform, particularly in crossing the 'grain' of the country, one must be equally conscious of the parts played by river-erosion and structure in the shaping of the land-surface. The two are inseparable.

It will be as well, then, to begin with some examples of a simple scarp-and-vale type of landscape. Communications aligned along the strike of the rocks present no great problem. It is the crossing of the alternating outcrops which is liable to be difficult.

Present river-valleys and the relics of past river-valleys may permit roads and railways to pass through a cuesta with a minimum of interference. The water-gaps in the North Downs are perhaps the best-known examples; the lines of communication have become very markedly concentrated on them. The Stour, Medway, Darent, Mole, and Wey all pass through the Chalk cuesta by well-marked valleys containing road and railway. Between the Darent and the Mole, however, no present-day river-valley is available, and since this is the section which is nearest to London and which stands in the way of important lines of communication to the South Coast, roads and railways have had to be carried across it by more difficult routes. The summit of the cuesta is not everywhere of uniform height and the communications have tended to select the lowest crossing-points. Even so none of the four railways concerned is able to make the crossing except by the use of summit tunnels, all of them over a mile in length, at Merstham (2), Oxted, and Polhill.

On the other side of the London Basin there is an even longer section of the Chalk cuesta (the Chilterns) unbroken by a water-gap, and here the railways and many of the roads approaching London make use of dry gaps (so-called 'wind-gaps'), as, for instance, at Princes Risborough, Wendover, and Tring. Further to the north-east the A.5 road passes through the dry gap at the head of the Ver valley, while the Hemel Hempstead–Leighton Buzzard road (B.486) follows that of the Gade. Among well-known water-gaps which have become important as passages for communications one could cite the gap in the Lincolnshire Limestone at Lincoln, and those of the rivers which break through the South Downs to the Sussex coast. The breach made in the Cotswolds by the Bristol Avon has provided a route for road, rail, and canal (Plate 22). There are few counties in which examples could not be found (Plate 23).

Photo: Aerofilms

PLATE 22. THE AVON VALLEY NEAR MONKTON COMBE, SOMERSET

This water-gap through the Jurassic cuesta of the southern Cotswolds carries road, railway, and canal in the difficult approach to the city of Bath from the south-east. Although the valley is circuitous, the intervening surface of the Great Oolite has been so dissected by the Midford Brook and its tributaries that even the road (A.36, Salisbury–Bristol) can be found accompanying the Trowbridge–Bath railway and the Kennet & Avon Canal. View to the north.

The influence of scarplands on the railways has been very clearly brought out by S. H. Beaver.[1] By combining the gradient profiles of railways with a geological section, he has shown the relationship between them. His representation of part of the former Midland main line from St. Pancras is reproduced in Figure 10. The

[1] S. H. Beaver, 'Geography from a railway train'. *Geography*, xxi (1936), p. 265.

Photo: Aerofilms

PLATE 23. TAFF'S WELL, GLAMORGAN

The twin water-gaps by which the Taff escapes through the upturned strata on the southern edge of the South Wales Coalfield. Note the concentration of communications on the gap, a concentration which, in the case of the railways, has been accentuated by the competition of rival companies. The Taff Vale Railway of 1836 (entering in the foreground) was the first of several. The Cardiff Railway (extreme right) also passed through on its way into the coalfield, while the branch of the Rhymney Railway can be seen diverging to the right from the Taff Vale Railway immediately beyond the long viaduct. This viaduct carried a branch of the Barry Railway eastwards to the Rhymney valley. As it has to cross the interfluves bounding the Taff valley on both sides, it maintains its height as best it can. The Cardiff–Merthyr road (A.470) is seen on the right and the linking road to Radyr (B.4262) on the left. Between the main road and the Taff Vale Railway lies the bush-lined course of the derelict Glamorganshire Canal. View to the north-north-west.

general direction of the line is the same as that of the dip of the rocks, and under these conditions the switchback effect of the crossing of the scarplands is most clearly seen. But all of the railways into London in the north-western sector exhibit these features to some extent and the principal summits can generally be correlated with particular geological outcrops as well as with the water-partings between drainage-systems. On the Chalk are found the summits at Saunderton, Wendover, Tring, Leagrave, and the less clearly defined summits at Stevenage and Woolmer Green. The Great Oolite is crossed at Roade and Sharnbrook, the Inferior Oolite at Desborough. Roade and Sharnbrook represent also the water-partings between Ouse and Nene drainage, Desborough the water-parting between Nene and Welland, and so on.

These correlations are based on the recognition of successive outcrops of rock sweeping across the English lowlands. In detail, however, such outcrops may be highly irregular, especially where

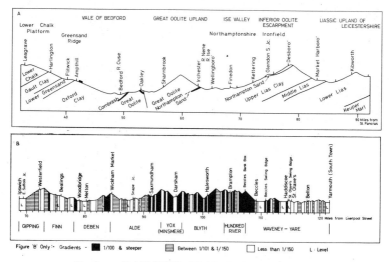

FIG. 10. RAILWAY GRADIENT PROFILES

A. Part of the main line of the former Midland Railway, showing geological section. After S. H. Beaver, 'Geography from a railway train', *Geog.* vol. 21 (1936).

B. The East Suffolk line (Ipswich to Yarmouth), showing drainage systems below. Based on *Gradients of the British Main Line Railways.*

the angle of dip is very gentle. Then are found heavily indented scarp-faces, outliers on hill-tops separated from the main outcrop, and older rocks exposed in the rear of the scarp-face in the valley-bottoms. In such circumstances the relationship between communications and geology may be equally pronounced but of a somewhat different kind or rather on a different scale. It is exemplified, for instance, in the tunnels on the main line of the former Midland Railway from St. Pancras to Nottingham, via Melton Mowbray (Fig. 11). The divisions shown on the map are

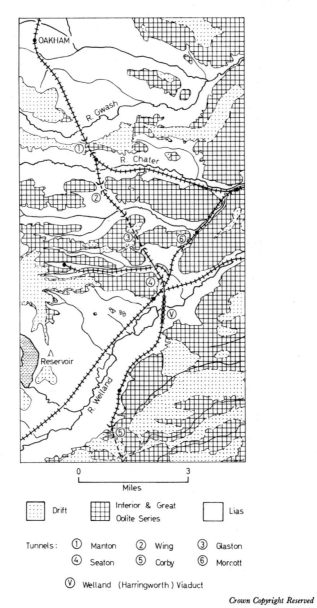

FIG. 11. RAIL TUNNELS, DRAINAGE, AND GEOLOGY IN PART OF THE WELLAND VALLEY ON THE RUTLAND–NORTHAMPTON-SHIRE BORDER

made according to the age and not the composition of the rocks, which are by no means uniform in each category, but in general the Lias consists of clays, shales, and other rocks which have been more easily eroded, while the oolites include the Northampton Sand Ironstones as well as limestones, and these tend to be more resistant to the processes of denudation. The drainage pattern consists of parallel streams, flowing eastward more or less down the dip, which have cut valleys into the Lias leaving relics of the Oolite on the interfluves.

Coming south from Oakham the line enters the valley of the Gwash by a cutting, just outflanking the capping of Northampton Sands. The next interfluve is capped by faulted outcrops of Northampton Sands and limestones of the Inferior Oolite Series as well as drift, and as this cannot be outflanked it is pierced by the Manton Tunnel. This gives access to the Chater valley, along which the original line, completed between Leicester and Peterborough in 1849, turns eastwards towards Stamford. The present main line, completed in 1880, continues across the Chater to pass through the next interfluve by the Wing Tunnel, the exact crossing-point corresponding with a marked dip in the skyline where the Northampton Sands have been breached to expose the Lias. The next interfluve is again capped mainly by the Northampton Sands and is penetrated by the Glaston Tunnel, beyond which a slight eastward salient enables the line to outflank the oolite cap on which Seaton village stands, and the short Seaton Tunnel through the Lias Clay emerges half-way up the side of the Welland valley. So far, apart from a short climb from Manton to Wing, the line has been falling almost continuously from Oakham. Even so on reaching the Welland valley it is still well above river-level, and the viaduct by which it is carried across its flood-plain is one of the most spectacular in Britain. Once across the valley the line immediately begins the climb, mostly at 1 in 200, by which it passes over into the Nene drainage-system, but not until it has once more tunnelled under the Inferior Oolite Series, the escarpment of which here corresponds with the right-bank slopes of the Welland valley.

The task of surmounting a cuesta may be simplified if the line of railway approaches it diagonally. The line from Craven Arms to Much Wenlock (Shropshire), for instance, crossed the Wenlock Limestone escarpment by climbing diagonally up the scarp-face near Major's Leap. Perhaps a more familiar example is that which occurs on the East Coast main line between Retford and Tuxford (Nottinghamshire), where a low but conspicuous escarpment is formed by narrow bands of sandstone in the Keuper Marl. The railway makes a slight eastward salient at this point in order to be able to surmount the escarpment at a narrow angle (Fig. 12).

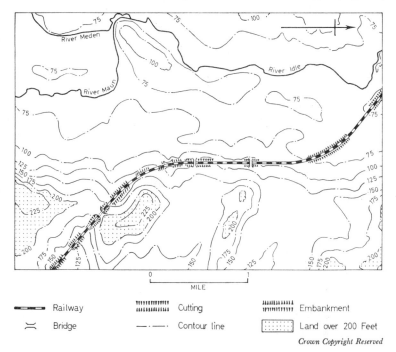

Railway	Cutting	Embankment
Bridge	Contour line	Land over 200 Feet

Crown Copyright Reserved

FIG. 12. THE EAST COAST MAIN LINE SURMOUNTING A LOW ESCARPMENT NEAR EAST RETFORD, NOTTS

But where the direction of the line is at right angles to the scarp-face its surmounting often necessitates the provision of long embankments. A good example occurs at Scunthorpe (N. Lincolnshire). After crossing the Trent at Althorpe Station the railway runs due east and at right angles to the escarpment of the Lower Lias which lies some two miles from the river. The escarpment is less than 200 feet high, but even so the line has to begin climbing almost at once on embankment and viaduct. In this way it hits the scarp-face rather more than half-way up, and a cutting then suffices to carry it through to Scunthorpe Station which lies on the dipslope.

A dozen miles further north a similar feature can be seen on the

former Hull & Barnsley Railway. The obstacle here is more formidable than at Scunthorpe. The low Jurassic escarpment at
North Cave is immediately succeeded by the Chalk of the Yorkshire Wolds rising to about 500 feet. A cross-section of this double

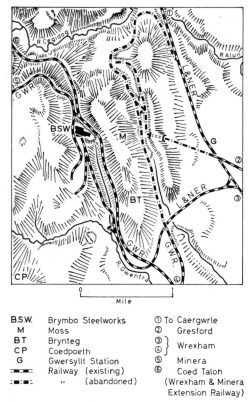

B.S.W.	Brymbo Steelworks	① To Caergwrle
M	Moss	② Gresford
BT	Brynteg	③ ⎫
CP	Coedpoeth	④ ⎬ Wrexham
G	Gwersyllt Station	⑤ Minera
▬■▬■▬	Railway (existing)	⑥ Coed Talon
:■:■:	,, (abandoned)	(Wrexham & Minera Extension Railway)

FIG. 13. RAILWAYS AT BRYMBO, NEAR WREXHAM,
DENBIGHSHIRE

escarpment shows the usual asymmetry, the steep western scarp-
faces contrasting sharply with the gentle dipslope to the east. Unfortunately, however, since the railway was intended primarily
for the movement of coal from the Barnsley Coalfield to Hull, it
was to be expected that the general pattern of traffic would be
made up of heavy, loaded coal-trains going east and lighter
empties returning. It was therefore necessary to reverse the
asymmetry provided by nature, and the gradient up to the Drew-
ton Tunnel from the west, that is up the scarp-face, was made

slightly less severe than that up the dipslope. The long and prominent embankment which can be seen rising above the Walling
Fen is the instrument by which this was achieved.

The crossing of the Yorkshire Wolds at this point would have
been unnecessary but for the fact that the easier passages at
Market Weighton and in the Humber Gap were already occupied
by a rival company's lines. The obstacle could not therefore be
outflanked. To the north-west of Wrexham (Denbighshire), by
contrast, there is a fascinating little piece of scarp-and-vale
country which, though very small, is economically so important
that it has attracted several railways into it (Fig. 13). The cuestas
are steep, rather than high, and short enough to be outflanked and
penetrated along the strike by the intervening vales. The resulting
pattern merits some further description.

The rocks of the Carboniferous system resting on the Ordovician and Silurian of North-Central Wales, dip generally eastwards under the plain of north Shropshire and Cheshire. The lower
members of the system, Carboniferous Limestone and Millstone
Grit (Cefn-y-fedw Sandstone), outcrop in the Eglwyseg and
Ruabon Mountains respectively, and the Grit reappears to the
north-west in the Moel Garegog. Most of the workable coals are
contained in the Middle Coal Measures which succeed the Grit
and outcrop roughly along a line from Cefn Mawr through
Rhosllanerchrugog, Coedpoeth, and Brymbo towards Caergwrle.
Within the Middle Coal Measures, which are predominantly
shaly, are found 'sandy shales and sandstones . . . the principal
sandy bed being the Cefn Rock'.[2] In Hercynian times the whole
of this area was subjected to vigorous faulting which was

accompanied, or more probably was followed, by mineralization of
many of the fault belts. Metallic ores occur abundantly along the . . .
Carboniferous outcrop . . .; these are almost completely restricted to
the Carboniferous Limestone and the overlying Cefn-y-fedw Sandstone. . . .[3] The chief minerals are lead sulphide (galena)—with a
little silver—and zinc sulphide (blende), with which are associated
copper pyrites and fluorspar.[4]

The faulting has also fractured the Middle Coal Measures so that
the tiny strike streams in the neighbourhood of Brymbo, Moss,
and Brynteg having carved away the softer shales, the Cefn Rock
appears in more than one intervening cuesta. The coal which lies

[2] Bernard Smith and T. Neville George, *British Regional Geology, North Wales*
(2nd ed. 1948), p. 64.
[3] Not to be confused with the Cefn Rock.   [4] Smith and George, op. cit., p. 68.

under this close little landscape of scarp and vale has given rise to a dense network of communications, some of which have penetrated further westwards to reach the metalliferous deposits of Minera.

The railway system has been complicated by the fact that more than one railway company was interested in the area. No less than three of the 'Big Four' reached Brymbo: the Great Western from Wrexham continuing to Minera, the L.N.E.R. with its line from Gwersyllt (part of a group of railways acquired by the Great Central in North Wales early in the century), and the L.M.S.R., by virtue of its half-share in the Wrexham & Minera Extension line from Coed Talon. These railways and their colliery branches exhibit a remarkable parallelism, being aligned from north-north-west to south-south-east, that is to say fitting rigidly into the grain of the scarplands.

The road system is less precisely related to the structure, and appears at first sight to consist of a labyrinth of lanes and minor roads connecting up the semi-scattered settlements of the coalfield. But on closer inspection these roads too can be seen to follow a definite trend in the same direction.

In these examples of scarplands the geological structure has emphasized and largely determined the nature of the interfluves between the river-valleys. Even where there is no such structural pattern, there may be no less difficulty in bringing a railway across the line of drainage, as can be seen from the main line between London (Liverpool Street) and Yarmouth, particularly in the section north of Ipswich. The surface here takes the form of a low plateau of Pliocene and Pleistocene rocks overlying the Chalk and tilting gently towards the east and south-east. The main features of the drainage pattern, which consists of small parallel streams running in an easterly to south-easterly direction, were developed on a surface of glacial deposits and are therefore comparatively new in age. Even so there has been ample time for these numerous streams to cut well-defined and often steep-sided valleys in the soft and poorly consolidated rocks. The lower parts of these valleys were without exception flooded in the Neolithic submergence[5] and although many of the resulting estuaries have now been filled in by alluvium, those of the Orwell, Deben, Alde, and Blyth have not, and these compelled the Ipswich–Yarmouth railway to follow a course well inland from the coast, and at right angles to the lines

[5] J. A. Steers, 'The East Anglian Coast'. *G.J.* lxix (1927), p. 24.

of drainage. The result is the alternate crossing of valley and inter-fluve, and the gradients of this line, though short, are quite severe, at least as far as Beccles. The continuation to Yarmouth is able to make some use of the alluvium of the Waveney, which here under-goes a sharp change of direction and flows parallel with the coast, but even including this section some fourteen miles (26·5 per cent.) of the Ipswich–Yarmouth line are built at gradients steeper than 1 in 100 while another 13·8 miles (26·1 per cent.) are at gradients between 1 in 100 and 1 in 149. That is to say over half the line is steeper than 1 in 150 (Fig. 10B).

It is in these conditions of rapid alternations of altitude that the susceptibility of railways to quite small variations in relief is best brought out. The influence of this kind of country on the roads can be dealt with more briefly, but perhaps it would be appropriate first to take one comparative example which brings out very clearly the different potentialities of road and railway when con-fronted by a piece of country exhibiting this rapid alternation of valley and interfluve. The surface of Anglesey consists largely of a great Tertiary platform known as the Menaian Platform, above which project a few isolated monadnocks. The 'strike' of the rocks, which vary from Pre-Cambrian to Carboniferous in age, is from north-east to south-west and this corresponds roughly with the dominant direction of ice-movement, so that there is today a very pronounced effect of graining, with numerous parallel valleys alternating between the relics of the Menaian Platform. The plat-form itself slopes gently from about 300 feet in the north-east of the island to 150 feet or less in the south-west.[6]

Early in the nineteenth century the main road across the island to Holyhead via Llangefni was superseded by a new trunk road which Telford laid out as part of the government's improved route for the Irish Mail traffic.[7] This work included the provision of the Menai Bridge, and from this point to the crossing to Holy Island Telford followed a comparatively straight line, ignoring the county town of Llangefni and making only small deviations to minimize the effect of some of the physical obstacles. The rises to 200 feet at Gaerwen and to 250 or thereabouts at Llangristiolus and Gwalchmai could be surmounted quite easily by this splendid coach-road which forms part of the present A.5 trunk.

[6] A. D. Lewis, 'Anglesey' (*The Land of Britain*, ed. L. Dudley Stamp), (1940), p. 220.
[7] A. H. Dodd, *The Industrial Revolution in North Wales* (2nd ed. 1951).

In 1844 and 1845 the Chester & Holyhead Railway was authorized. From Llanfair P.G. westwards Robert Stephenson followed Telford's road for about two miles, but from this point onwards the relief which had proved passable for the road was too strong for the railway. Stephenson was therefore obliged to strike further south where the Menaian Platform (and hence the surfaces of the interfluves) is somewhat lower, and here, by using numerous cuttings and two short tunnels near Bodorgan, it was possible to find a reasonable route. The reasons for the divergence of the main road and railway as they cross the island become apparent only if one understands the nature of the relief and the different demands put upon it by the two forms of transport.

The comparative freedom of physical control enjoyed by the Holyhead road (A.5) beyond the Menai Straits certainly does not apply to its passage across the Welsh mainland. Its course through Snowdonia is rigidly controlled by the glaciated valleys, and from Capel Curig to Llangollen it follows a great trough-like depression which, though drained at present by more than one river-system, almost certainly represents the ancient valley of the River Dee.[8] Stronger relief brings with it a stronger influence on the pattern of roads. In the Scottish Highlands, for instance, the slogan 'one valley one road' would generally be found valid. Even in the lowlands this is partly true. The roads from Carter Bar to Selkirk and from Jedburgh to St. Boswells provide links from the Border northwards 'across the grain' of the country, but apart from these the main roads hereabouts reflect strongly the 'dendritic' drainage pattern of the Middle and Upper Tweed system. But even in Upland Britain road-systems have been developed freely across quite formidable barriers where the economic necessity has justified them. In the area to the north-east of Manchester the high Pennine watershed is crossed by five 'A' class roads at an average interval of two miles and at altitudes between 1,270 and 1,600 feet. Again in South Wales modern engineering has shown that the uplands of the Pennant Grit, which sealed off the Rhondda valley from its neighbouring drainage-systems, are not an insuperable obstacle to the good motor roads which now connect it with the head of the Cynon valley on the north and with the Avon and Ogmore valleys on the south.

[8] H. R. Wilkinson and S. Gregory, 'Aspects of the evolution of the drainage pattern of North-east Wales'. *Liverpool & Manchester Geol. Journal*, vol. 1, part 6 (1956), p. 543.

In Lowland Britain this physiographic independence is still more pronounced. All the main escarpments are freely crossed by main roads, and the correlation between road lines and geological structure is expressed in terms of water-partings as often as of river-valleys. Davies, distinguishing between 'dip roads' and 'strike roads' in the Croydon area,[9] brings out some interesting facets of geological control over routeways, but one is not left with the impression that the relief is in any sense prohibitive. After citing the use of the Merstham Gap at 432 feet by the Brighton Road (A.23), Davies goes on to mention the alternative Brighton Road (A.217) which 'ascends the Chalk dipslope, crossing Banstead Downs and Burgh Heath and climbing to nearly 700 feet above sea-level before descending the escarpment at Reigate Hill, where a cutting at the summit and a detour down the hillside render the gradient less difficult than might be expected'.[10] Again, some of the features he describes have an apparent geological significance which is really subordinate to other considerations. For instance the statement that 'in the Chalk area south-east of Croydon the predominance of "dip" over "strike" roads is noticeable'[11] is true enough, but this would in any case be expected in this situation as a matter of economic geography, since the strike of the rocks is here tangential to the radial roads leading out from London.

The influence of structure and drainage-systems on canals is particularly strong. There are many similarities between the canals and the railways from this point of view. For instance, in crossing many of the great escarpments canals and railways have shown the same response to the relief by adopting similar courses. This is well brought out by some of the big tunnels. At Harecastle (N. Staffordshire) canal and railway pass together under the watershed between the Trent and Mersey systems; at Sapperton (Gloucestershire), they cross the Cotswold escarpment which separates Thames from Severn; at Standedge (Yorkshire) the canal tunnel lies parallel with the railway tunnels under the Millstone Grit (Plate 24). Or again a very strong physical landscape, such as that of the South Wales Coalfield, imparts to both railway and canal alike a pattern which directly reflects the drainage. But since the canals have different requirements in making use of a land-surface, so their passage from one drainage-system to

[9] G. M. Davies, 'Geology and lines of transport in the Croydon District'. *Trans. Croydon Nat. Hist. & Scientific Soc.* ix, part 4 (1923–5), p. 187.
[10] ibid., p. 190.
[11] ibid.

Photo: Kenneth Field

PLATE 24. THE STANDEDGE TUNNELS

This impressive concentration of communications is to be seen at Marsden, Yorkshire, where the railway and canal, having followed the Colne valley up from Huddersfield, plunge into the three-mile long tunnels which carry them under the Millstone Grit moorlands of the main Pennine water-parting. The earliest railway tunnel is in the centre. The left-hand tunnel was added later when the track was doubled. Later still the double-track bore was added to complete the quadrupling between Huddersfield and Stalybridge. The Huddersfield Narrow Canal is here at the highest level of any canal in Britain (638 feet O.D.). The main tunnel entrance lies below and to the left of the large railway bore and is approached obliquely from the right of the double-track line. The main road from Huddersfield to Oldham (A.62) climbs diagonally above the tunnel mouths to reach a summit-level nearly twice as high as that of the canal. Note the mounds of material excavated from the tunnels. View to south-west.

another tends to be something more complicated, and certainly more circuitous than that of a railway. Furthermore there are three other considerations which have a bearing on the route followed by a canal and which are intimately bound up with this question of structure and drainage.

In the first place the rivers, which have been the instruments in shaping the land-surface, may themselves be elements in a system of water communications. The canal companies in Yorkshire, for instance, made periodic use of rivers such as the Aire, Calder, and Don, modifying and dredging them, and in places providing cut-offs and new alignments. Similarly the Trent, the Soar, the Weaver, and many others are lines of communication in their own right and largely control the position of the waterways in their valleys. It is worth noting that this inevitably means an attraction of the canals towards the valley-bottoms and may well conflict with the principle that it is easiest to follow the contour lines along the valley-side.

In the second place canals are vitally concerned with water-supply, and this again is something which may be controlled by the drainage pattern itself. Where a canal is confined to one river-valley, such as are many of the small canals of the West Country, it is sufficient to be able to secure a supply of water at the upper terminus of the canal, and if this lies in the valley-bottom there is no physical problem in providing one. The Lea and Stort Naviga-tions had their upper termini at Hertford and Bishop's Stortford respectively where the rivers concerned were already adequate as sources of water-supply. But where a canal has to pass from one drainage-system to another the problem is more difficult. In this case the summit level will occur at (or very near to) the watershed between the drainage-systems, which is the worst possible place for feeding it with water. It very often happens that, since the watershed is generally crossed at its lowest point, some small stream can be found a little further along it at a slightly higher altitude where a reservoir can be constructed, but the available collecting-ground necessarily tends to be small. Examples of this kind of feeding reservoir can be seen at several places along the main watershed of central England (Fig. 16). Further south the Grand Junction Canal was provided with a group of reservoirs[12] near Tring summit (Plate 25), where it crosses the Chilterns, in a position where they can take advantage of the spring-line at the foot of the Chiltern scarp. Unfortunately, however, this could only be achieved at a level slightly below that of the summit-pound (391 feet), so that pumping is necessary. A similar situation arises at Crofton, near Savernake, where the Kennet valley and the Vale of Pewsey are separated by Chalk uplands, and the filling of the summit-pound of the Kennet & Avon Canal had to be carried out by pumping.[13]

---

[12] Tringford, Marsworth, Startopsend, and Wilstone (Fig. 14B).
[13] L. A. Edwards, *Inland Waterways of G.B. and Northern Ireland* (1950), p. 142.

Photo: J. K. St. Joseph, by permission of the Committee for Aerial Photography, University of Cambridge, and of the Air Ministry
Crown Copyright Reserved

PLATE 25. CANALS AND RESERVOIRS NEAR MARSWORTH, BUCKINGHAMSHIRE

These reservoirs, with a fourth at Wilstone (beyond the right-hand margin of the picture), provide the water-supply for the southern section of the former Grand Junction Canal between the Thames and the Great Ouse. The canal is seen in the foreground rising from right to left through three of the locks in the flight which carries it to the summit pound, about a quarter of a mile beyond the left-hand margin (Fig. 14B). These reservoirs are situated where the canal crosses the spring-line at the foot of the Chiltern scarp. The canal in the distance is the abandoned Wendover branch and the loop which it describes (top right-hand corner) is highly characteristic of a 'contour canal' crossing the valley of a small stream. View to the south-south-west.

This brings us to the third point, which is that outcrops of permeable rock may present the canal engineer with special difficulties which would be irrelevant, perhaps even advantageous, to the surveyor of roads or railways, in so far as the canals themselves, and not only their reservoirs, are more easily accommodated in impermeable strata.

Of course it is always possible to line a canal with an impermeable material and this has frequently been done—at a price. But there are examples of permeable rocks proving difficult. Hadfield records that the Thames & Severn Canal had 'a summit level through the Great Oolite that throughout its long life lost up to three million gallons of water a day in leakage . . .'[14] and that '. . . the Salisbury and Southampton built part of its line, and then failed to make a cut that would hold water through the Bagshot Sand deposits between the watersheds of the Test and Avon, and the whole canal was abandoned after the proprietors had spent nearly £100,000.'[15]

With these points in mind the next step is to look more closely at one of the most interesting areas in the whole canal system of Britain, the head of the (Warwickshire) Avon valley (Fig. 16). This salient of the Severn drainage-system into the Triassic and Jurassic scarplands is bounded by watersheds with other drainage-systems leading in very different directions: on the north the Blythe, Anker, and Soar, all feeding into the Trent, on the east the Welland, Nene (with its tributary the Ise), and Great Ouse all feeding independently into the Wash, and on the south the Cherwell which joins the Thames at Oxford. The strongest relief is found along the watershed which separates the Avon from the Cherwell and the rivers of the Wash, which is not surprising since it is now known that the Avon–Anker and Avon–Soar water-partings were formed when glacial reversals of drainage took place and therefore date only from the Pleistocene,[16] and also since the water-partings on the eastern and south-eastern side of the Avon roughly coincide with the strike of the rocks and are reinforced by cuestas.

The earliest trunk connexion between London and the Midlands was provided by the Oxford Canal, the course of which has obviously been strongly influenced by the drainage pattern. It is significant that it enters the Avon system direct from that of the Cherwell by the Fenny Compton Gap at 377 feet above O.D. (Fig. 14A). That is to say as far as this point it lies wholly within a single drainage-system (Cherwell–Thames). Once through the gap, it swings north-east and follows the scarp-foot to the neighbourhood of Rugby, falling in two stages (at Napton and Hillmorton) to a level of 303 feet which it maintains to its junction

[14] Charles Hadfield, *British Canals* (1950), p. 79.
[15] ibid., p. 99.
[16] Up to this time the present Upper Avon valley was drained north-eastwards towards the Trent by a headstream of the Soar. G. H. Dury, 'A 400-foot bench in south-eastern Warwickshire'. *P.G.A.* 62 (1951), p. 167.

F. W. Shotton, 'The Pleistocene deposits of the area between Coventry, Rugby and Leamington and their bearing upon the topographic development of the Midlands'. *Phil. Trans. Royal Soc.*, B, 237 (1954), p. 209.

with the Coventry Canal at Hawkesbury, the lowest point anywhere on the upper Avon watershed. This route is physiographically by far the easiest between the Thames and the Trent systems,
but it is not very direct, because the Avon system pushes it much
too far to the north-east for a trunk line between London and
Birmingham, while the Thames system pushes it too far to the
south-west.

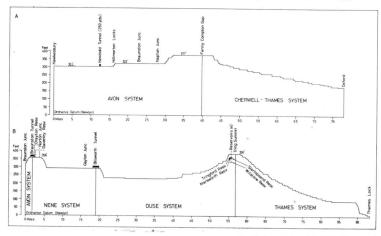

By kind permission of British Waterways

FIG. 14. CANAL PROFILES

A. The Oxford Canal from its junction with the Coventry Canal at Hawkes-
   bury to the Thames at Oxford.
B. The Grand Junction Canal from Braunston (junction with the Oxford
   Canal) to Brentford (Thames Lock).

The shortening of this route involved two major stages, both of
which necessitated a departure from the physiographic optimum
represented by the Oxford route. The first of these was the provision of a route from Napton direct to Birmingham by the Warwick & Napton and Warwick & Birmingham Canals (Fig. 15A).
This required a fall to 176 feet at the Avon crossing and a climb
again to the watershed at Kingswood, the next lowest passage
across the Upper Avon watershed after Hawkesbury. The second
great project was the Grand Junction Canal which, by keeping to
the east of the Thames–Cherwell system, encountered both the
Ouse and the Nene drainage-basins before it could reach the
Oxford Canal in the Avon basin (Fig. 14B). Tunnelling was
necessary under both the Ouse–Nene and Nene–Avon water-

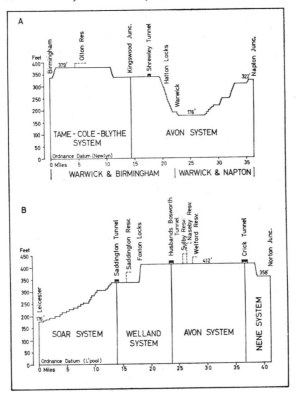

FIG. 15. CANAL PROFILES

A. The Warwick & Birmingham and Warwick & Napton Canals. Birmingham
   (Digbeth) to Napton Junction on the Oxford Canal.
B. The Leicester Canal. Leicester to Norton Junction on the Grand Junction
   Canal.

sheds. This shorter route from London to Birmingham was provided, therefore, at the expense of heavy engineering undertakings and a multiplicity of locks, and it is interesting to note that
it was at one time proposed to built a canal[17] to connect the Warwick & Birmingham near Kingswood with the head of the Coventry
Canal at Coventry and thereby overcome some of these difficulties.
This partial reversion towards the route of the Oxford Canal,
though a few miles longer, 'would have reduced the number of
locks between Birmingham and Braunston from fifty-four to
seventeen by avoiding the heavy lockage down to and up from
the Avon valley at Warwick'.[18]

[17] The Central Union Canal.   [18] Hadfield, op. cit., p. 147.

When one looks at the map (Fig. 16) the canals seem to fall into physical sections, each of which can be equated with a drainage-system, and this is the key to an understanding of how the canals have used this piece of country. Whereas in a simple valley canal,

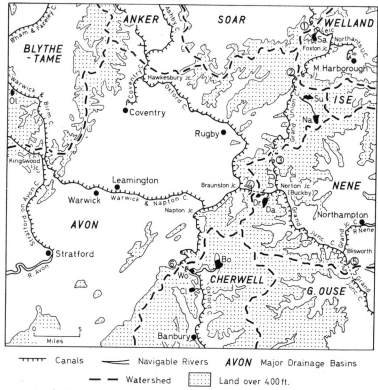

Canals   Navigable Rivers   *AVON* Major Drainage Basins

Watershed   Land over 400 ft.

Tunnels :- ① Saddington ② Husband's Bosworth ③ Crick ④ Braunston ⑤ Blisworth
⑥ Fenny Compton (former)

Reservoirs:- Sa. Saddington Su. Sulby Na. Naseby Dr. Drayton Da. Daventry
Bo. Boddington Wo. Wormleighton Cl. Clattercote Ol. Olton

Crown Copyright Reserved

Fig. 16. CANALS AND WATERSHEDS IN THE (WARWICKSHIRE)
AVON AND ADJACENT DRAINAGE-SYSTEMS

such as the Brecon & Abergavenny in the Usk valley, it is the contours along the valley-*sides* which suggest a level route, in this Upper Avon area it is the contours looping round the valley-*heads* which are crucial. Since the rivers run outwards from a roughly north–south axis of upland, the valley-head contours collectively open up the easiest possibilities for a trunk line along the axis, so that a barge passing, say, from London to Leicester progresses along the valley-head contours of one drainage-system after another, the Ouse, the Nene, the Avon, and the Welland. Only when it reaches the Soar system does it find a valley where the *side*-contours are running in the right direction, and by that time the contours have to be abandoned for the valley-bottom, since it is the Soar itself which continues the line of communication to the Trent.

These Midland scarplands are not severe enough to evoke a similar response in the railways which by rising and falling more freely are able to cross the watersheds with much less deviation. But bolder relief can produce a strikingly similar form of 'valley-head progression'. A good example occurs in the Settle & Carlisle Railway (Fig. 17). This railway, completed in 1875–6, was designed to provide a route by which the Midland Railway could reach Carlisle independently of the London & North Western and its associated company the Lancaster & Carlisle. These two latter companies owned the West Coast main line which occupied the lower land on the west of the Pennines, and the Midland Railway was therefore forced to look further to the east for a routeway. The line as constructed from Settle Junction follows Ribblesdale to Ribblehead Station where it passes into the Greta valley by what would appear to be the abandoned valley of a headstream of the Greta captured by the Ribble. Next it is carried by tunnel under Blea Moor into Dentdale and again by tunnel under Rise Hill into Garsdale from which it crosses the principal watershed into Wensleydale, again using an abandoned valley immediately above an elbow of capture near Garsdale Station. Finally at Ais Gill Summit the line enters the Eden valley which it follows to Carlisle. In short in a total distance of some thirteen miles the line finds itself in the valleys of the Ribble, flowing to Preston, three tributaries of the Lune, flowing to Morecambe Bay, the Ure flowing to the Humber, and the Eden flowing to the Solway Firth.

Although the relief of the Pennines is strong, their effect as a barrier is minimized by the relationship which exists between the systems of the Ure, the Lune, and the Eden. This is the product of river-capture aided and abetted by a somewhat complicated glacial history,[19] and it has little in common with the Jurassic

---

[19] W. B. R. King, 'River Captures in the Lunds, Yorkshire'. *The Naturalist* (1924), pp. 41 and 81.

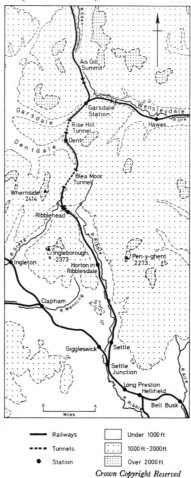

——— Railways	☐ Under 1000 ft.
▪▪▪▪ Tunnels	☐ 1000 ft.-2000 ft.
● Station	☐ Over 2000 ft.

Crown Copyright Reserved

FIG. 17. PART OF THE SETTLE & CARLISLE LINE, FORMER
MIDLAND RAILWAY

Scarplands round the headwaters of the Nene, Ouse, Cherwell,
and Avon. Nevertheless there is a striking point of comparison
between the Settle & Carlisle line and the Grand Junction Canal.
The course of the railway from Blea Moor Tunnel to Ais Gill is
comparatively level. One could almost call it a 'contour line'. But
the appropriate contours occur, not in one valley, but peripherally
round the heads of separate valleys, and it was by picking them
up and following them for short distances that Crossley was able
to find his route through the Pennines exactly as the various

engineers of the canals in the East Midland scarplands had done sixty to a hundred years earlier.

Undoubtedly the most striking example of a pattern of communications being controlled by a drainage-system to be found anywhere in Britain is that which occurs in the South Wales Coalfield. The pattern reaches its maximum development in the eastern part of the field and on the northern side of the main synclinal axis. The Taff, Bargoed Taff, Bargoed Rhymney, Rhymney, Sirhowy, Ebbw Fawr, and Ebbw Fach all run from north-north-west to south-south-east. Further west the Cynon, Clydach, Rhondda Fach, and Rhondda Fawr pursue a rather more easterly course (Fig. 18).

Just as the Cefn Rock in the Wrexham Coalfield appears above the main productive coal seams, so in South Wales the Pennant Grit is found in a roughly comparable stratigraphical situation. But it is thicker and altogether more massive than the Cefn Rock and resembles more closely the Millstone Grit of the Pennines in that it gives rise to large tracts of bare moorland rising to altitudes between 1,000 and 2,000 feet. Most of the unique characteristics of the South Wales Coalfield, its patterns of settlement, industry, and not least communications, derive from this simple geological fact, that, whereas in the coalfields of the North of England the massive grits lie below the Coal Measures (and therefore crop out off the coalfields), in South Wales they lie on top of the coal[20] which has to be reached through the deep gashes cut by the rivers.

The northern escarpment of the Pennant Grit has been so vigorously carved up by these river-valleys that east of Hirwaun Common it is difficult to identify it on the map. The parallel contours which generally make the identification of escarpments an easy matter give place to a series of nose-like projections between each valley. But when seen from the west or the north-east this Pennant escarpment, fragmented as it is, appears as one of the most prominent and well-developed in Britain. Below the escarpment the iron-bearing outcrop of the Lower Coal Series has given rise not only to the long line of derelict ironworks from Merthyr Tydfil eastwards but also to a comparatively easy routeway across the base of the escarpment. This is followed by the A.465 trunk road as well as (formerly) by the Merthyr, Tredegar & Abergavenny line. These communications, linking the old ironworking

[20] There are coal seams of economic value above the Pennant Grit but their extent and productivity are far more limited than those of the lower seams.

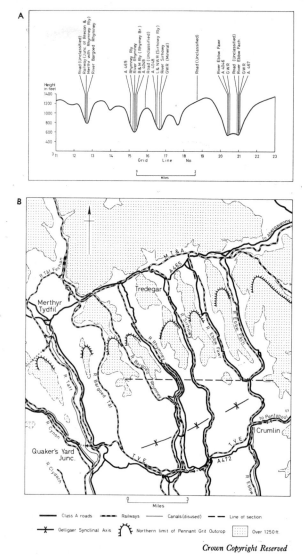

FIG. 18. PART OF THE SOUTH WALES COALFIELD

A. Section along grid-line 2_{02} North, between grid-lines 3_{11} and 3_{23} East. Drawn from the 1 : 25,000 Ordnance Survey map and not instrumentally surveyed.

B. Map of the communications in the area between Merthyr Tydfil and Ebbw Vale.

towns, approximately mark off the upward extremity of industrialization in each of the valleys they cross. For some distance to the south of this the interfluves of Pennant Grit are so high that lateral communication between the valleys is virtually impossible. Only when the axis of the Gelligaer Syncline is approached does the Pennant surface come low enough to permit relatively easy movement from east to west and here it is crossed by the A.472 road and the Taff Vale Extension line of the original Newport, Abergavenny & Hereford (later G.W.R.) from the neighbourhood of Quaker's Yard to Pontypool. It is between this routeway and that which follows the outcrop of the Lower Coal Series (Merthyr–Abergavenny) that the parallel development of valley-settlement and valley-route reaches its extreme form. East of the Taff systems, in which the Glamorganshire Canal reached Merthyr (and Aberdare in the tributary Cynon valley), the penetration of the valleys by canals was restricted to the lower parts of the Ebbw valley (to Crumlin) and Cwmavon. But the branching system of early wagonways which was used to feed them formed the basis of the later railway system. Eventually most of these valleys came to be occupied by railways and roads, which are often duplicated on either side.

Although it would be incorrect to describe these valleys as 'consequent', since they have been superimposed from a higher surface, long ago removed by denudation, the direction of the drainage lines here follows the direction of the dipslope rather than the strike. Therefore the element of parallelism in the pattern of communications, while it is reminiscent of the parallelism in, for instance, the Wrexham scarplands, previously described, reflects an entirely different relationship to the geological structure.

In this and the preceding chapters I have tried to show that the physiographic basis of communications is more complicated, sometimes more indirect, and perhaps more subtle than is at first apparent. It will be as well, therefore, to sum up with an example which illustrates as well as any how paradoxical the relationship can be. Figure 19 shows all the railway tunnels in Great Britain over a mile in length, including those which have now been closed, but excluding those of the London Underground system. One might be tempted to suppose that there is a correlation between relief and the occurrence of long rail tunnels, and so there is. But this is not to say that the hillier areas are necessarily the places to look for the long tunnels. The median line of latitude between the northern and southern extremities of the British mainland runs approximately from the southern end of Coniston Water to Scalby Ness, Scarborough. It is true that this line does not divide the area of the mainland into equal parts. The northern part is the smaller, but it contains by far the greater amount of really rugged

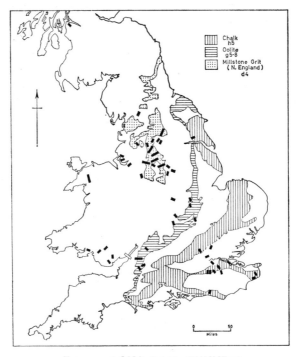

FIG. 19. LONG RAIL TUNNELS

Short lines denote tunnels more than one mile but less than two miles long. Long lines denote tunnels more than two miles long. Open symbols denote estuarine tunnels. Urban 'Underground' railway tunnels omitted.

Source: 'The Railway Year Book', 1932

highland and all the land over 3,000 feet except for a few hundred acres in Snowdonia. Yet of the fifty-three long rail tunnels shown in Figure 19, no less than fifty-two lie to the south of this line, and the solitary exception is situated between the Boundary Faults within the so-called Midland Valley of Scotland. The Highlands, Southern Uplands, and Lake District furnish no examples at all.

Mere elevation, therefore, hardly provides any clue to the interpretation of this map. Neither does the geological map do more than suggest certain correlations between the occurrence of long tunnels and some particular rock outcrops. There are, perhaps, two main propositions which throw light on this distribution. The first is that long tunnels tend to occur where heavy concentrations of population are found within, or immediately adjacent to, areas of sharp relief. Being tied down to objectives within the hilly tracts, the railways are less able to overcome physical obstacles by avoiding them altogether or by selecting the easiest routes through them, as they can in passing through barriers like the Southern Uplands which contain few large urban centres such as would give rise to the necessity for inter-connexion by direct lines. This aspect of the question is especially important in the southern Pennines and in South Wales, and to a lesser extent on Mersey-side and Thames-side. It explains also the lone Scottish example which, lying under the back streets of Greenock, allowed the Caledonian Railway to reach Gourock Pier, a task which it could easily have accomplished along the narrow lowland fringing the Clyde but for the prior occupation of this site by the town centre. Similarly numerous shorter tunnels, not shown on the map, are to be found in towns throughout the country, even in areas of low relief. Salisbury, Ipswich, and Newmarket are examples.

The second proposition is that long tunnels tend to be necessary where alternations of relief, though not necessarily great, are sudden, particularly where the landforms which give rise to them are not of purely local extent, and where the lie of the land does not afford the opportunity of a gradually ascending approach. The tunnels of the Jurassic scarplands and of the cuestas peripheral to the Weald come in this category. Indeed most of the tunnels in the heavily populated areas, especially the southern Pennines, are explicable only in terms of both these propositions. Figure 19, then, is not as paradoxical as it may at first have appeared; rather it tends to bear out what has already been discussed in the physical field. It is now time to turn to other lines of investigation.

CHAPTER V

THE FORM AND FUNCTION OF COMMUNICATIONS

Figure 20 shows the road-systems in the immediate approaches to two towns, Crewe and Norwich, and the striking contrast between them is immediately apparent. Even allowing for the fact that Norwich has more than twice the population of Crewe, it is obvious that the road-pattern of Norwich allows a far more direct accessibility into the surrounding countryside than does that of Crewe. Physiographically there is no serious impediment to the development of roads in either place. Both towns are situated in areas of comparative lowland. If anything, there are more physical obstacles in the case of Norwich, yet these have not prevented the development of a system of roads spreading out like the spokes of a wheel in almost every direction.

Although, as has been shown, physical features often exert a strong influence on the location of communications they can hardly ever be described as the causes of their construction. They are permissive or prohibitive, as the case may be, and they can show either property in varying degrees, but lines of communication will not be built unless there is some economic demand for them, no matter how favourable the physical setting may be. The nature of the economic requirement may vary a great deal. It may not be 'economic' at all in the strict financial sense of the word. Military requirements, for instance, would have to be included.

From the example of Crewe and Norwich three important points emerge. The first is that lines of communication, like any other element in the landscape, invariably reflect in their shape, arrangement, and pattern the purpose for which they were made. In different terms we can say that there is a correlation between function and form or morphology. Norwich is perhaps the best example of a provincial regional centre anywhere in England. It is a small, local capital of an agricultural area within which all those activities which are centralized at all are centralized in this country town. Its nearest rival is Ipswich, forty-five miles away.

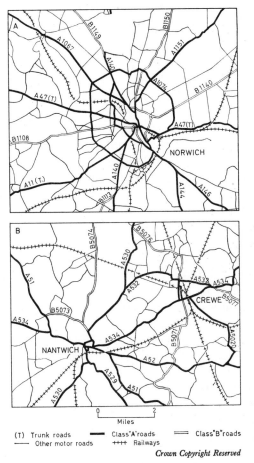

(T) Trunk roads   ▬▬ Class"A"roads   ══ Class"B"roads
—— Other motor roads   ++++ Railways

Crown Copyright Reserved

FIG. 20. RADIAL ROAD AND RAIL PATTERNS

A. Norwich
B. Crewe

Crewe, on the other hand, has very few such activities. It certainly acts as a local market and retail centre for part of the Cheshire plain, but in many ways it is eclipsed by its neighbours. It lies between the county town of Chester and the industrial con-urbation of the Potteries, and on the northern side it is dwarfed by Manchester. It enjoys a different function from Norwich and this difference emerges in the road map.

Economic geography, however, is never permanent. The con-ditions which have given rise to one pattern of communications may not persist. Communications which are a product of one period may pass on as elements in the landscape of a succeeding period to which they may or may not be able to adapt themselves. There are, in fact, innumerable bits and pieces of roads, canals, and railways lying about here and there which are simply incomprehensible in terms of modern economic conditions, and it is imperative to understand how the pattern of the present has grown out of the pattern of the past. This is the second point. In 1830 there was not even a hamlet where Crewe stands today. If it had been even a small market town at that date one would have expected to find a more complete system of roads linking it with the villages which it served. There is in fact just such a pattern, but it is centred on Nantwich, an old market town four miles to the south-west, and now only a sixth of the size of Crewe. Norwich, on the other hand, by 1830 already had behind it centuries of industrial and commercial prosperity during which it had established itself as a regional capital and had acquired a network of roads suited to its function and status.

The third point is no less important. The statement that Crewe has not the same radiating pattern of communications as Norwich must be confined to the roads. Its railways exhibit this pattern very strongly, more so, in fact, than those of Norwich. In other words, what applies to one kind of communication in a town does not necessarily apply to another. In this and the following chapter, therefore, these questions will be considered further, first by taking examples which illustrate the way in which the shapes and patterns of communications reflect their present functions, then by examining more specifically cases where the evolutionary aspect is dominant, at the same time noting some of the differences which apply to each particular kind of communication.

The relationship between form and function is perhaps most clearly brought out in the most simple case, that is where a line of communication is solely concerned with the movement of some commodity from one point of origin to one point of destination. In practice such forms are comparatively rare, since they tend to become complicated by the addition of extensions and by incorporation in larger networks. One can, however, find such simple systems in operation in mining areas, where the point of origin is the pit-head or quarry, and the destination some key-point in the wider communication system. Already, in fact, it becomes apparent that such units do not exist wholly in isolation but are related, at least at one end, to further communications. A good example of this is provided by the slate railways of Snowdonia which connect the slate-quarries with the ports. The most important of these quarries lie along an outcrop of Cambrian rocks on the north-western side of the Snowdon mountains and in the Ordovician rocks around Blaenau Ffestiniog to the south-east. These slate-belts are inland, and when their commercial exploitation began on a larger scale at the end of the eighteenth century and in the early part of the nineteenth, it was absolutely dependent on the provision of adequate links with the coast. These links took the form of narrow-gauge railways leading by the most direct practicable routes to potential port-sites. Although not all of these railways are still working in their entirety, this association of particular quarries with particular ports can still be followed on the Ordnance Survey maps and on the ground. Thus the Penrhyn quarries had their outlet at Port Penrhyn, the Dinorwic at Port Dinorwic, and the Ffestiniog at Portmadoc. Within the slate-belts the railways ultimately assumed branching forms by which they were able to tap different quarry faces, but to a large extent they retained their comparatively simple unilinear form.

The Northumberland–Durham Coalfield would provide other examples. The wagonways which reached the Tyne on both sides (some of which are still working) stretched out as direct and separate links between pits or groups of pits and staithes on the navigable river. The present Ordnance Survey one-inch map[1] shows two good examples, the Pontop and Jarrow and Pontop and South Shields branches. They can be seen crossing the East Coast main line a little to the north and south of Birtley respectively.

The same essential simplicity of form can be found also in some canals, especially where they have penetrated inland along small river-systems such as those of the Torridge or Exe, or where they are large-scale, expensive waterways, designed to reach a particular destination from which further distribution can be achieved by other means. The Manchester and the Gloucester & Berkeley Ship Canals are examples. In Manchester, for instance, the concentration and dispersal of traffic is carried out almost wholly by other forms of transport. The ship canal is merely the artery by which this traffic is moved *en bloc* between the sea and Salford Docks, where trans-shipment takes place.

[1] Sheet 78, Newcastle-upon-Tyne. The names still appeared in the New Popular Edition (1947) but are omitted in the Seventh Series (1953).

The other extreme is to be found in the road-pattern, which, in most of Britain, takes the form of a freely inter-communicating system of parts, so that it is more difficult, and indeed often impossible, to identify particular units in the pattern as having functions which can be as precisely identified and defined as those of, say, the North Wales slate railways. Furthermore, the railway

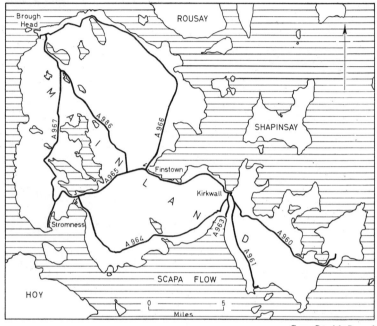

FIG. 21. 'A' ROADS ON THE MAINLAND OF ORKNEY

and canal systems also generally exhibit the same features to a lesser degree, those which have already been quoted having been chosen as exceptional rather than typical. When one begins to analyse these more complicated networks, however, one finds innumerable ways in which their various components have distinctive properties reflecting recognizable functions.

The most distinctive pattern is the radial form as in Norwich, but for one reason or another it may be distorted or only imperfectly developed. For instance the road-pattern of the Mainland of Orkney is unmistakably radial, being centred on Kirkwall (Fig. 21), but owing to the restrictions imposed by the shape of the island it is a lop-sided figure. To the east and west there is some opportunity for a fanning-out of the roads; to the south there is very little (the Scapa Bay road, A.963, 1½ miles long, must be one of the shortest 'A' class roads in Britain), and to the north there is none at all. The Mainland of Shetland has an even more strait-jacketed system, drawn out along the length of the island, yet just recognizable as radial on Lerwick.

A very common feature associated with the communications of large towns is the ring road. We have already noted the road-pattern of Norwich as consisting of a spoke-like figure with the city as the hub. This structure is clearly suited to a concentration of all traffic on a central point, from which through traffic can then be diverted on to the right channel for the next part of its journey. The system is analogous to that of a telephone exchange, which is entirely dependent on the concentration of all the lines at ᵔne point where inter-connexion is made as required. With the enormous increase in modern road traffic, however, this in-evitably results in congestion, and, to reduce this, new com-ponents are added to the road-system which make it possible for such inter-communication to be achieved without reaching the huᵇ. Such roads are sometimes called 'orbital' by comparison with the spokes, which are called 'radial'.

An examination of the road-system of almost any town will reveal some orbital development of this sort, though it may assume different forms. It is almost entirely a product of the modern age, being designed to cope with a situation which has only arisen on a large scale since the revival of road transport following the development of the internal combustion engine. In some towns, however, these orbital routes have been built up from pre-existing parts which were made originally to serve other functions. Traffic is directed along 'ring roads' from one radial road to another and thus makes its way round the town centre. These roads may be indistinguishable in appearance from other parallel residential roads and yet carry many times more traffic. The roads of 'better-class' late Victorian residential districts are often used for the purpose, partly because they tended to lie on what was then the periphery of the town and partly because they were invariably more spacious in their proportions and could therefore be better adapted to their new function, but almost any kind of road may be pressed into service for this purpose. Another common feature of this type of ring road is its discontinuity where it crosses the radial roads. Since the roads were not built for orbital traffic, there was no particular point in their being immediately opposite to each other. Even where modern outer ring roads are available one may find inner ring roads of this kind. Nearly all British towns furnish some examples.

But where the volume of traffic justifies it, an entirely new orbital road-system may be provided. Such by-pass roads generally continue directly across the radial roads, often being provided

Photo: Aerofilms

PLATE 26. MAIDSTONE BY-PASS (KENT) UNDER CONSTRUCTION

The line of route just clears the northern outskirts of the town. In the foreground is the intersection with the Sittingbourne road (A.249). View to the west-north-west.

with roundabouts at the intersections. Where the traffic of one main road through the town is dominant, this may show itself in the form and layout of the road and be readily apparent on the map. The North Oxford By-pass, for instance, is in effect a realignment of the London–South Wales road (A.40), and is at the same time so positioned as to give the easiest possible access to the Stratford road (A.34). The dominant direction of traffic-flow through Winchester could be guessed from the position of the by-pass to lie between Southampton Water and the Home

Counties. A similar influence may be seen in the by-passes at Ashford (Kent), Shrewsbury, Colchester, and many other places. The form reflects the function (Plate 26).

In all these examples by-passes represent attempts to overcome

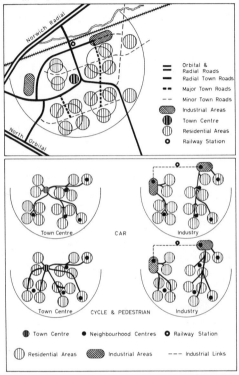

FIG. 22. ROAD-PATTERNS AND METHODS OF CIRCULATION IN HARLOW NEW TOWN, ESSEX

Based on diagrams in the Master Plan, Harlow New Town, 2nd ed., 1952

the problems raised by modern traffic having otherwise to use the streets of old towns totally unsuited to the purpose. Where, however, the street plan has been laid out since the road transport revolution, it can be constructed in such a way as to serve most efficiently the modern transport needs of the town. The special demands of vehicular traffic can be anticipated and a system devised which will meet them. Figure 22 shows in diagrammatic form how directly the planning of the road-pattern in one of the New Towns springs from a consideration of the probable traffic circulation.

The concentration of traffic in towns can just as easily lead to congestion on the railways as on the roads, and here also the by-pass is quite a usual device, though it is not generally known by this name. 'Avoiding-lines' are often found where there is a consider-able volume of through traffic which does not have occasion to stop at the town in question. This applies primarily to goods traffic, which is nothing but a nuisance in a busy passenger station. Doncaster, for instance, is an important junction for passenger traffic. It also lies in the path of a busy coal traffic which has no need to pass into the station at all. A complete system of avoiding-lines has grown up, whereby mineral trains can be carried across the main lines by over-bridges with a minimum of interference to their traffic.[2] A similar combination of heavy passenger and mineral traffic may be seen in Wigan, where both the former L.N.W.R. and L. & Y. systems had avoiding-lines. In Lincoln passenger train working in the stations has always been linked with a severe road problem owing to the level-crossings, and the avoiding-line on the south of the city is used to provide relief. Short avoiding-lines carrying main lines past busy stations may be found at Bedford, Didcot, Westbury, Frome, Gloucester, and elsewhere. In larger towns they may become so fully developed as to form a 'circle' line, as in London and Manchester.

Where two or more lines converge on a station from the same side they may be connected by a direct link or spur so that through running can take place between them. In such a case the avoid-ance of the station is not the primary objective and may even be a disadvantage. Thus the Bristol–Hereford–Crewe expresses pass well within the built-up area of Newport (Monmouthshire) but use the curve at Maindee to pass direct from the Bristol–Newport to the Newport–Hereford line without being able to enter Newport Station (Plate 27). Spurs in comparable situations may be seen at Derby and on the south side of Preston. One of the most curious is at Ely (Fig. 23B). Here there is a good deal of direct traffic between the March and Norwich lines. The York–Yarmouth services, for instance, use this route. The provision of a direct link between the two lines was here complicated by the presence of the King's Lynn line, which bisects the junction between the Norwich and March lines. The simplest way out was therefore

[2] J. H. Appleton, 'The railway network of southern Yorkshire'. *I.B.G., Trans. & Papers*, 22 (1956), p. 159.

Photo: Aerofilms

PLATE 27. NEWPORT, MONMOUTHSHIRE

The town centre is on the right bank of the Usk (nearest camera). Beyond the river the railway line to Bristol and Gloucester (right) diverges from that to Abergavenny, Hereford, and Crewe (left). The Maindee Curve can be seen connecting the two. Through trains between the Bristol and Hereford lines cannot use Newport Station unless they undergo reversal. The 'Eastern Valleys' line of the former Monmouthshire Railway enters from the left and passes under the main line between the station and the Usk Bridge. View towards the east.

to commence the new line beyond (south of) the junction and describe three parts of a circle before joining the March line, a solution which also permits through running if necessary between the King's Lynn and March lines. Other complicated patterns of loops and spurs which are related to the provision of through parts between converging tracks may be seen at Trent Junction (Plate 33). Here the details are somewhat different, but the purpose is to provide the maximum opportunity for through running between five converging lines. Fortunately the flood-plain of the Trent provides an ample exercise-ground for these manœuvres.

The relationship between form and function which can be seen in these examples at Ely, Trent, etc., is expressed in the provision of inter-connecting lines which afford the maximum opportunity

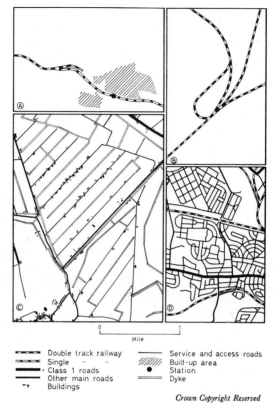

Double track railway   Service and access roads
Single   "   "   Built-up area
Class 1 roads   Station
Other main roads   Dyke
Buildings

Crown Copyright Reserved

FIG. 23. PATTERNS OF ROADS AND RAILWAYS

A. Railways in Cockermouth, Cumberland.
B. Railways at Ely, Cambs.
C. Roads in Fodder Fen, near Ely, Cambs.
D. Roads at Hillington, Renfrewshire. Contrast the rectilinear pattern to the
   north of the railway line (the Trading Estate) with the curvilinear pat-
   tern to the south (the Housing Estate).

Details from O.S. 1/25,000 maps

for the flow of traffic between converging railways. Sometimes,
however, the traffic of two crossing lines is in the main quite
separate and here the negative aspect of their relationship may
be equally clearly brought out by the absence of such facilities
for the interchange of traffic. Both the West and East Coast main
lines to Scotland pass through the areas of comparative lowland
which separate the coalfields and textile districts of south Lancashire and west Yorkshire from the ports on the Irish and North

Seas respectively. Such traffic as passes from these main lines to the ports of Liverpool or Hull or to the inland centres of Manchester, Leeds, etc., leaves them well to the south at Crewe, or Weaver Junction or Doncaster, as the case may be, or, if it is traffic between these places and the North, the separation takes place at Preston or Euxton, Northallerton or York. But there is also a totally different traffic between the inland towns and the ports, which is not at all concerned with the north–south main lines. So the West Coast line at Warrington is crossed by the two lines of the former C.L.C. between Manchester and Liverpool, the crossings being by over-bridges, with no connecting-links to the main lines (see Fig. 24). A little further north at Earlestown the main line joined the original Liverpool & Manchester Railway and here actually used its metals for over a mile as far as Parkside, so that interchange between north–south and east–west lines could and regularly did take place.

But with the development of more direct communications from London to Liverpool (via Runcorn) and Manchester (via Wilmslow), this interchange, which involved the crossing of the two kinds of traffic on the level, became more of a nuisance than an asset, so that the present main line between Winwick Junction and Golborne Junction eliminates this common section and passes directly under the Liverpool & Manchester line. A little further north again the former Great Central line to St. Helens crosses by over-bridge, again with no spur lines for interchange of traffic, and a mile short of Wigan the former L. & Y. avoiding-line does the same thing.

Similarly the East Coast line between Heck and Temple Hirst is crossed first by the former Hull and Barnsley then by the former L. & Y. (Wakefield, Pontefract, and Goole). In neither case is any contact made with the main line. At Joan Croft, four miles north of Doncaster, a spur was inserted to connect with the West Riding and Grimsby line, but the mineral line which crosses a little to the south (former Hull & Barnsley and North-Eastern Joint) has no means of contact with the main line.

All these are examples of the intersections of separate channels, dealing with the conveyance of different traffics in different directions and this finds expression in the forms of the intersections.

The relationship between the form and function of canals can perhaps be best illustrated by comparing the systems of the former Birmingham Canal and Grand Junction Canal Companies. The

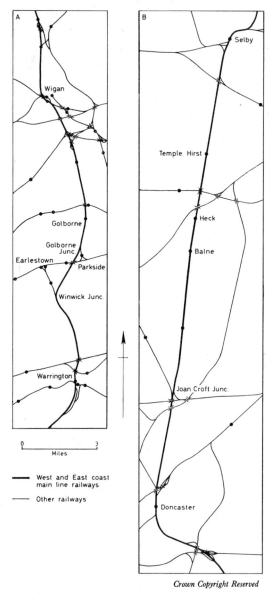

FIG. 24. RAILWAYS: PARTS OF THE WEST COAST AND EAST COAST
MAIN LINES

A. The West Coast main line and connexions in South Lancashire.
B. The East Coast main line and connexions in South Yorkshire.

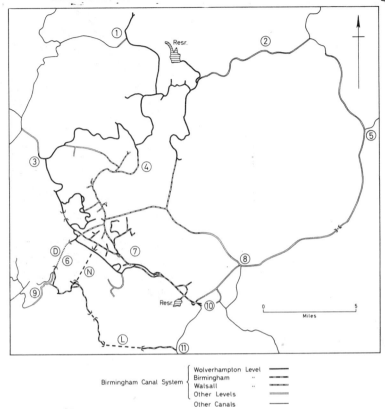

FIG. 25. THE BIRMINGHAM CANAL SYSTEM, c. 1924

1. Cannock. 2. Lichfield. 3. Wolverhampton. 4. Walsall. 5. Fazeley.
6. Dudley. 7. West Bromwich. 8. Salford Junction. 9. Brierley Hill. 10.
Birmingham. 11. Selly Oak.

Tunnels: D. Dudley. N. Netherton. L. Lappal.

*Based on a Map of 1924 (T. A. Henshaw and H. K. S.
Woodhouse), by courtesy of British Transport Waterways*

Birmingham, as eventually constituted, comprised about 160 miles
of waterway,[3] the Grand Junction about 125, excluding its extension, the Regent's Canal. But whereas the Grand Junction
stretched over a direct distance of some seventy miles between its
termini, the Birmingham system was condensed into an area about
twenty miles long by a dozen broad. Within this area was concentrated an intricate network of waterways (Fig. 25). From a

[3] C. Hadfield, *British Canals* (1950), p. 87.

G.C.—K

ramification of inter-connecting cuts there stretched out numerous tiny terminal branches, many not more than a few hundred yards in length with some 550 private basins.[4] In the triangle between Stourbridge, Wolverhampton, and Lichfield there was hardly a single point as much as two miles from a canal. By contrast the Grand Junction Canal had few branches. Much the greater part of its mileage was taken up in the main line between Brentford and Braunston. The whole shape and disposition of the properties of these two companies were entirely different. The Grand Junction was mainly concerned in the movement of long-distance traffic, much of which travelled over the greater part of its main line, while the Birmingham performed the service of providing local accessibility to the numerous industrial premises of the Black Country. By it they could be connected with the main canal systems of the country and with each other, but more particularly with the railways, whose policy 'was to use the canal like a road, for a collection and delivery service'.[5]

An important aspect of the function of any line of communication is its capacity, and this very frequently finds expression in its form. By 'capacity' is meant the number of vehicles or trains of vehicles which can be moved over a given section in a given period, such as 'a thousand vehicles per hour'. The capacity of a line of communication is generally related as closely as possible to anticipated traffic, since lines of greater capacity are invariably more expensive to construct, and obviously it is pointless to go to unnecessary expense. It does not follow, however, that the anticipation of traffic will necessarily be correct, nor that a volume of traffic, once achieved, will necessarily be maintained.

The correlation between capacity and volume of traffic is therefore only approximate and in some instances the two are manifestly out of balance. Furthermore, unless an even flow of traffic is maintained round the clock and throughout the year the full capacity will only be achieved for short periods. It is safe to say that this question of peak load capacity is the thorniest with which the traffic planners have to deal. If congestion is to be avoided it is necessary to fit capacity to the *maximum* volume of traffic likely to be encountered under normal circumstances.

The capacity of a road is arrived at by a theoretical assumption about the speed of vehicles, together with the number of lanes of traffic which can be accommodated. Most British main roads are

---

[4] G. Hadfield, *British Canals* (1950), p. 188.   [5] ibid., p. 189.

of single carriageway type with room for one lane of traffic in each direction. Higher capacities can be achieved with three and four lanes. Where the traffic justifies it, the modern practice is to build dual carriageways. On the new motorways these will generally each be 24 feet in width. The first section of the London to Yorkshire Motorway has each carriageway 36 feet wide (see Chapter IX). In the Highlands of Scotland, on the other hand, many 'A' class roads are wide enough only for single-line traffic, and passing-places are provided which are inter-visible from each other, so that the roads can be used for traffic in both directions and yet can be constructed more cheaply than two-lane roads.

The capacity of railway lines is rather more complicated to assess, since the use of the 'block' system of signalling, which is ubiquitous on lines used for passenger traffic and is practised on many goods lines as well, introduces another variable, namely the length of the block, which is generally the same thing as the distance between signal boxes. Most main lines are of double track, the capacity of which is more than twice that of single track, since operating is not affected by reversals of direction and the necessity for holding back trains in passing-places. The effective capacity of a line will also vary with the efficiency of operating techniques. For instance, successive trains travelling at the same speed can be passed along a line in one direction more easily than trains running at greatly differing speeds. Casual observation of the traffic between, say, King's Cross and Peterborough, where line capacity is affected by a number of 'bottlenecks', will show that it is normal practice to group express passenger trains as far as possible, and between each group to use the lines for slower-moving traffic.

Where traffic is heavy enough, four tracks may be needed. The main line from Euston, for instance, is of four tracks as far as Roade, some sixty miles out. The seventy-five mile section from St. Pancras to Glendon North Junction, near Kettering, is alleged to be the longest continuous stretch of four-track line in the country. Numerous shorter sections of railway with four and more tracks are to be found, for instance, in the industrial North.

The appearance of the track may therefore give an immediate clue to the importance of a railway as assessed by the volume of traffic it can carry, but sometimes tracks which are in effect of a 'duplicate' nature may follow a different course and yet achieve much the same function. At Sharnbrook Summit, for instance, the four-track main line of the former Midland is divided into two lines of two tracks each, which diverge from each other, as can easily be seen on the one-inch map.[6] One crosses the summit in tunnel, the other in the open. The reason lies in the fact that, when the two-track line was quadrupled, advantage was taken of the opportunity to build the newer track on different gradients better suited to the requirements of the goods traffic for which it was intended. Here the divergence between the two tracks is slight. With wider divergence it becomes impossible to say when a track is the duplicate of another line and when it becomes an entirely separate railway. The Northampton Loop, for instance, is used partly as a duplicate to the Roade–Rugby section of the main line. In West Yorkshire the Heckmondwike Loop performs a similar function for the Leeds–Huddersfield line. Yet both serve separate towns and villages *en route*.

Often the capacities of lines are increased by doubling or quadrupling only in those sections where this can be done at reasonable cost. Then intervening narrow sections limit the total line capacity. Sections of this sort are generally associated with physical obstacles, where the construction costs are greatly increased. The double-track line from Worcester to Hereford, for instance, is reduced to single track where it passes by tunnels under the Malvern Hills near Colwall (Plate 28) and again under the lesser hills which lie across its path where an anticline has thrown up the Silurian rocks at Ledbury. At Saltash, west of Plymouth, the main line to Penzance is narrowed to single track for rather more than half a mile where it crosses the Tamar by Brunel's Royal Albert Bridge.

Just as greater volumes of traffic may give rise to larger, more efficient, more capacious lines of communication, so they may bring about an increase in the density of a network of communications. A railway map of Britain would be quite a good rough guide to the distribution of population. But it could never be more than approximate. The intensification of the mesh in some particular parts is not merely a product of population density or of industrial development. This is an important topic in the geography of communications and it will be discussed further in Chapter VII.

It will be apparent from what has been said that many facets of this relationship between form and function find expression on the

---

[6] O.S. 1-inch map, sheets 133 and 134.

PLATE 28. THE
MALVERN TUNNEL,
WORCESTERSHIRE–
HEREFORDSHIRE
BORDER

Between Malvern Wells (top)
and Colwall Station (bottom)
the Worcester–Hereford line,
of double-track, narrows to
single-track to pass by tunnel
through the Malvern hills
which lie across its path.
East-north-east at the top.

map, and any experienced map-reader should be able to go a long
way towards deducing the function or purpose of a line of communication from its position on the map, taking into consideration all the other features which are shown. Consider, for instance,
some of the branch-line railways by which docks are connected
with main lines, particularly in towns where the main lines
approach from, or converge on a side of the town remote from
the docks or river-wharves. The dock railways in King's Lynn[7]
reach the Ouse waterfront by a kind of pincer movement on either
side of the old town centre. In Hull[8] the concentration of railway
approaches on the western side of the town has given rise to the
development there of the marshalling yards. But the deep-water
docks lie downstream, that is on the eastern side. Direct communication through the old town centre would be impracticable
for several reasons including the difficulties which would result
from the bridging of the River Hull (a very busy line of water-
communication to industrial sites in the city) near its mouth, and
the link between docks and marshalling yards is therefore represented on the map by the two semi-circles of railway which
surround the town on its northern side. One of these discharges
the additional function of connecting the Hornsea and Withernsea
lines with the main (Paragon) station, but the essential function in
relation to the docks is clear enough from the map.

All the ports of the Firth of Forth provide opportunities for
studying this particular facet of the subject, though the ways in
which it finds expression are very different in each case. At
Grangemouth the whole settlement is based on the pattern of
canal, railway, and dock. At the other extreme one finds in Alloa
a concentration of railways on the northern side of the town connected with the dock by a tenuous line of railway which winds
its way through the town streets, a feature reminiscent of a very
different type of port in Weymouth (Dorset). On a larger scale a
similar problem arises in London where the North London Railway and the Regent's Canal were both provided for the same
purpose, to connect the main lines in north-west London (the
London & North Western Railway and the Grand Junction
Canal) with the docks.

Often the function of a small branch line will be obvious from
its relationship to some industrial premises named on the map.
The Merrybent Railway, for instance, on the south-western side

[7] Sheet 124.   [8] Sheet 99.

of Darlington, pursues a course some six miles long and terminates in an 'old quarry'.[9] On Thorne Moors, Yorkshire,[10] there are two different kinds of mineral line, distinguished not by any difference in the symbol used, but by their origins and destinations. One of these, two miles north-east of Thorne, is short and direct and connects the Doncaster–Hull line with a colliery which is marked on the map. Its purpose is obvious enough. But to the east of it a separate system of railways is shown consisting of a roughly rectilinear pattern of branch lines which appear to achieve nothing before they disappear beyond the eastern edge of the map. If, however, we pick them up on the next sheet[11] we find that they converge on a 'Peat Works', and the ramifications of the light railway then become explicable. The term 'Thorne Moors', of course, is here used in the old sense and refers to the peat fen.

Again, travellers on the main line to King's Cross may have noticed near Great Ponton, some four miles south of Grantham, a small branch line joining the railway at the northern end of the Stoke Tunnel. If they were to follow this on the Ordnance Survey map[12] they would see that it connects the main line with the Melton Mowbray–Bourne line near South Witham but only after describing the most elaborate convolutions in the neighbourhood of Stainby and Colsterworth. Again if they were to look carefully they would find that the map marks sidings parallel with the main lines at either end, a feature not always associated with terminal junctions of small branch lines. In fact this little railway carries a considerable traffic in ironstone. The ironstone quarries are marked on the map near Colsterworth village, and there is nearly always plenty of evidence to be seen in the sidings near Great Ponton in the shape of the specially constructed ore wagons which can easily be recognized whether full or empty. Ironstone railways are one of the most distinctive forms of communication.[13] Some examples from the Jurassic ironstone fields of the East Midlands are shown in Figure 26. These railways are normally required to collect ironstone from quarry faces which are gradually receding. The lines in the quarries tend therefore to change their positions while the delivery lines from the open-cast sites to the points of junction with the main line tend to be more permanent. Some curious shapes result.

[9] Sheet 85.   [10] Sheet 103.
[11] Sheet 104.   [12] Sheet 122.
[13] For a very detailed account of this type of railway see E. S. Tonks, *The Ironstone Railways and Tramways of the Midlands* (1959).

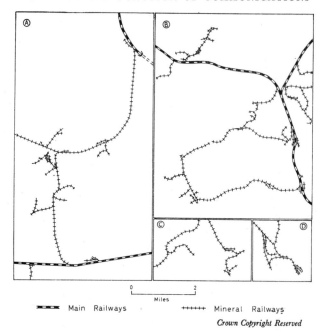

Main Railways   Mineral Railways

FIG. 26. MINERAL RAILWAY PATTERNS IN THE JURASSIC IRON-
STONE FIELDS

A. Stainby–Colsterworth area (Lincolnshire–Leicestershire–Rutland border).
   The junction in the north-east corner is with the East Coast main line
   immediately outside the Stoke Tunnel.
B. The environs of Kettering, Northants. The fork in the main line is at
   Glendon Junction. The Melton Mowbray–Nottingham loop strikes off to
   the north-east leaving the London (St. Pancras)–Leicester line at this
   point.
C. Denton, between Grantham and Belvoir Castle, on the Leicestershire–
   Lincolnshire border.
D. Cottesmore, near Oakham, Rutland.

The interpretation of roads along the same lines is generally
more difficult, because it is unusual for roads to be associated with
particular kinds of function in quite the same way. No doubt the
road approaches to open-cast coal sites are no less distinctive than
their railway counterparts, but they rarely assume the same length
or the same degree of permanence. An unusual example, however,
occurs at the Acorn Bank site in Northumberland, where a 30-foot
road has been constructed for a mile and a half to the Bebside
screening plant.[14] On its way it crosses two 'A'-class roads by over-

[14] 'Acorn Bank open-cast site'. *Colliery Engineering* (Sept. 1956).

bridges as well as the River Blyth, and provides a direct outlet for heavily loaded lorries independent of the public road-system. It is a simple and direct line of communication designed to fulfil a single particular function.

Among the distinctive types of road-pattern may be mentioned service roads and access roads, built solely to give access to property fronting on to them. As seen on the map they exhibit their

Photo: Aerofilms

PLATE 29. RESIDENTIAL ACCESS ROAD, STECHFORD, BIRMINGHAM

A highly elaborate, geometrical road pattern, characteristic of much inter-war 'estate' development. View near Stechford, Birmingham, looking east-north-east.

most distinctive form in inter-war, and to a lesser extent post-war, housing estates. The extraordinary patterns of circles, crescents, and less regular geometrical figures which such roads assume can be seen on the periphery of most British towns (Plate 29). Contrast this with a totally different yet no less distinctive type of service road, of a kind commonly seen in reclaimed fenlands. Numerous examples could be found in the Fens, but perhaps Fodder Fen is as good as any (Fig. 23c). It lies some four miles north of Ely.[15] The drainage has been carried out by cutting a series of parallel dykes. These dykes are too wide to be frequently bridged, and therefore they divide the land into long and independent rectangles, effectively isolated from each other. Clearly, then, a line running down the centre will afford the maximum degree of accessibility within each rectilinear strip, and this has been the ruling principle throughout. The roads are equidistant between the drains and the pattern of farms follows the roads.

Equally distinctive are the roads specially laid out in industrial and trading estates. Easy accessibility is essential, coupled with the necessity of fitting in to a systematic division of land for separate factory plots. A wide, rectilinear pattern usually results, as at Treforest and Bridgend (Glamorgan) or Team valley, Gateshead. At Hillington (Renfrewshire) the layout of roads is somewhat less regular, long sweeping curves being introduced to link two rectilinear road-patterns developed along different alignments. Even so there is a rigidity about the road-system in the industrial estate which contrasts with the florid, curvilinear pattern of the housing estate to the south of the railway line (Fig. 23D).

All these access or service roads represent communications on a local scale. It will be seen that this question of scale is of paramount importance. It is always pertinent to ask how far lines of communication are intended to serve local, regional, or national requirements, how far these may be combined in any one line, or how far separate channels have been provided for each type of transport need. This can be summed up by reference to the map of a small piece of country in north Lancashire (Fig. 27). Garstang, like many market towns, lies between contrasting types of country, the Forest of Bowland, which rises on the east to well over a thousand feet, and the plain of the Fylde on the west. It is connected by a network of roads with the villages of the lowland and the dispersed farmsteads which are scattered on the lower parts of the Forest of Bowland, up to about six or seven hundred feet. These are the local service roads. But Garstang also lies about half-way between the Lune on the north and the Ribble on the south in a direct line between Lancaster and Preston, the lowest respective bridging-points. These may be regarded as fixed points in the West Coast communication system. Routes passing further west cannot easily cross the estuaries. Further east they

[15] O.S. 1-inch map, sheet 135.

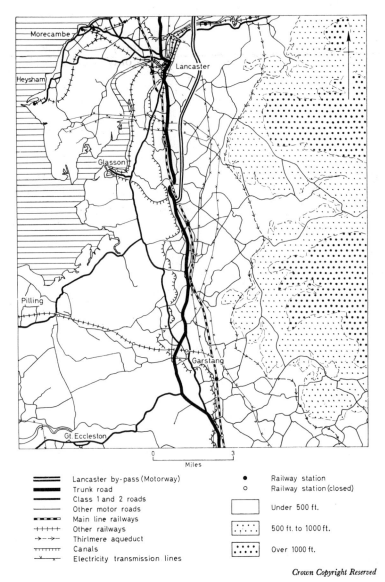

Lancaster by-pass (Motorway) ● Railway station
Trunk road ○ Railway station (closed)
Class 1 and 2 roads
Other motor roads □ Under 500 ft.
Main line railways
Other railways 500 ft. to 1000 ft.
Thirlmere aqueduct
Canals Over 1000 ft.
Electricity transmission lines

Crown Copyright Reserved

FIG. 27. THE COMMUNICATIONS OF THE GARSTANG AREA,
LANCASHIRE

Note the bunching together of trunk communications passing through the area
between the upland and the sea.

would become involved in the uplands of Bowland. They are therefore all bunched together in this strip of lowland. The Lancaster Canal passes the town incidentally on its way to the Lune. The West Coast main line now has only two stations open between Preston and Lancaster, namely Bay Horse and Garstang. The road (A.6) which once took the little market town in its stride, now assiduously avoids it by means of a modern by-pass which one could hardly fail to recognize from its shape and situation. The completion of the new motorway will introduce another unit even more effectively divorced from the local requirements of the district. Then there is the electricity grid which links the power stations of South Lancashire with those further north. Finally the aqueduct finds a suitable passage on its way from the Lake District to Manchester.

In other words the most important lines of communication in the area make very little contact with it and some of them none whatever, beyond using it as a means of passage between their origins and destinations. To see them in their true setting one should look at the Ordnance Survey one-inch map.[16] There can then be no doubt about the purposeful directness of these communications compared with the indecisive creeping-about of the minor roads across the face of the landscape.

[16] Sheet 94.

CHAPTER VI

EVOLUTION

It was emphasized in the last chapter that, while one can recognize a definite relationship between function and morphology in communications, more often than not this relationship can be only partly explained in terms of the present. The map of communications, as of other elements in the landscape, is built up of various pieces which are the residue of the economic geography of the past adapted to the requirements of succeeding ages. For a concise and lucid exposition of the way in which the English road-system is so derived one can do no better than turn to Hoskins' analysis of the road-system of the Banbury Sheet,[1] though it is essential in following his account to provide oneself with the map in question. In this account he selects various sections of road as shown on the map and traces their origins back to a very varied ancestry, which includes prehistoric trackways, Roman roads, local roads of the Dark and Middle Ages, long-distance routes associated with the droving of Welsh cattle, and so on. Although the period involved is much shorter, the same kind of argument can be applied to the ancestry of the railways, as I have attempted to show elsewhere.[2]

In the present context it seems better, rather than to review *seriatim* the contributions of each successive period, to confine our attention to a few important facets of the evolutionary process along the following lines. The heart of the matter is to be found in the nature of certain kinds of change and in the ensuing measures taken to meet them. Change always represents a challenge and this can be met only by the provision of new units or the adaptation of old ones. Both of these processes make their impact on the morphology of lines of communication. Furthermore they are subject to various influences, such as competition, private and public interest, finance, etc., which can profoundly affect the map of communications long after these influences themselves have ceased to apply. These ideas may help to put

[1] O.S. 1-inch map, sheet 145. W. G. Hoskins, *The Making of the English Landscape* (1955), Chapter VIII.
[2] J. H. Appleton, 'The Railway Network of Southern Yorkshire'. *I.B.G., Trans. & Papers*, 22 (1956), p. 159.

the geography of communications into its historical perspective in so far as this is necessary for an understanding of the present scene.

It will be as well to start by looking at the consequences of a major cultural change, that is to say comparing the demands made on the same piece of country, as far as transport requirements are concerned, by two communities living in different stages of cultural progress.

Those prehistoric trackways which can be traced for long distances almost always follow the outcrops of limestones or sandstones and in several cases are associated for mile after mile with particular cuestas. The ridgeways which follow the North and Berkshire Downs or the Jurassic stone-belt are among the best known. In cases like these not only did the well-drained land of these cuestas provide a suitable foundation for the road; it provided also a more acceptable environment for settlement in times when primitive communities had not the means to farm the wet clay-lands. In other words it is a reasonable inference that these trackways lay along axes of higher population-density, and such evidence as is available from the distribution of finds suggests that this was so.[3]

The Roman occupation brought with it a revolution not only in the techniques of road-making but also in the road requirements of the country. One must not envisage any immediate and wholesale change in the distribution of population or the abandonment of those trackways already in existence. Margary, for instance, believes that 'the ridgeways and primitive tracks were undoubtedly in constant use by the Romano-British population',[4] and many roads which have long been recognized as Roman are now known to be adaptations of older tracks. But the demand for increased accessibility for military and other purposes necessitated an entirely new concept of a road network which could no longer be based on the geological map, and although there are many Roman roads, such as Ermine Street on the Lincolnshire Limestone escarpment, which follow favourable outcrops, others were forced to adopt courses across the strike of the rocks and thereby encounter whatever obstacles nature interposed.

The situation in the Weald as worked out by Margary is illuminating. The North Downs Ridgeway and Pilgrims' Way

---

[3] See, for instance, W. F. Grimes, 'The Jurassic Way'. *Aspects of Archaeology in Great Britain. Essays presented to O. G. S. Crawford* (1951), p. 144.

[4] I. D. Margary, *Roman Ways in the Weald* (1948), p. 23.

represented the main pre-Roman thoroughfare on, or at the foot of, the Chalk escarpment, and in addition to this the Romans were able to use favourable geological outcrops for two new roads. The main London–Rochester–Canterbury road followed the bottom of the Chalk dipslope where it is overlain by the Thanet Sands at the base of the Eocene succession. Parallel with this to the south-west a branch from Rochester diverged to Maidstone, then followed the Lower Greensand for most of the way to the coast at Lympne. These roads between them placed London in direct communication with the group of Roman ports which lay at the narrowest crossing of the Straits of Dover. But to reach destinations further west along the Sussex Coast it was necessary to cross the central part of the Weald, the generally sandy rocks of which are surrounded by a belt of Weald Clay. In the sandier centre (Ashdown Forest, for instance) there was a network of trackways, one of which crossed the Weald Clay near Tonbridge. Margary distinguishes in addition four Roman roads which linked London with the Sussex coast, and which all had to face the crossing of the clays, namely from Maidstone towards Hastings, and from London to Lewes, Pevensey, etc., to Pycombe and Portslade (near Hove), and to Chichester. This last, Stane Street (Plate 30), crossed the western part of the Weald where the northern and southern outcrops of the Weald Clay swing round to join each other, and where the total width of the outcrop is at its maximum. From the southern edge of Dorking to Codmore Hill near Pulborough the road is on the clay continuously for a distance of some twenty miles. The surface is made up mainly of flint and gravel, but other materials such as sandstone and iron slag are found, for instance, at Alfoldean, where the road approaches nearest to the iron-bearing sandstones of the central Weald.

This picture of an urgent requirement of the *Imperium Romanum* for an adequate system of roads connecting London with the South Coast at frequent intervals reflects a major change of geographical values and an entirely different approach to the potentialities of the scarp-and-vale relief of the Weald. It is interesting to see just the same sort of values re-emerging with the next great resurgence of road-building in the turnpike age as described by Dr. Fuller in the same area.[5] The economic links between

[5] G. Joan Fuller, 'The development of roads in the Surrey–Sussex Weald and Coastlands between 1700 and 1900'. *I.B.G., Trans. & Papers*, 19 (1953), p. 37.

Photo: Aerofilm

PLATE 30. STANE STREET, SUSSEX

In the foreground the modern road (A.285) makes a deviation from the line of the Roman road to avoid the lower slopes of Halnaker Hill (left). The Roman road continues in a straight line to the edge of the Chalk escarpment (top right) which it descends at Bignor Hill. In the distance lies the low ground of the Weald Clay Vale. View to the north-east.

London and the South Coast were in many ways quite different from those of the Roman period, but the basic pattern of a road network radial on London and superimposed on an unco-operative geological surface suggests more points of similarity than of contrast. As one would expect, it is this second great phase of road-building which has mainly determined the outlines of the present system of main roads, though the Roman roads are well represented in it.

A different expression of this kind of geographical change may be found in the road-system round Salisbury. In the Roman period most of the settlement was still on the uplands of the Chalk. The present pattern of villages is largely Anglo-Saxon in origin and consists of mainly nucleated settlements in the valleys. The main roads of the area are to be found connecting these valley-settlements together and are therefore for the most part also closely related to the valleys. The remains of the Roman roads, however, can still be seen, and these are mostly to be found on the higher ground where also are innumerable signs of Celtic settlement. On close inspection, too, it will be seen that the Roman roads converge, not on Salisbury, but on the upland site of Old Sarum, some two miles to the north. Salisbury itself dates only from the early thirteenth century, and this is another reason why a new road-system has had to grow up independent of the Roman roads, though the latter are frequently followed by minor roads, and in the direction of Basingstoke, somewhat unexpectedly perhaps, by the railway.

In these examples one is confronted by what amounts to a comprehensive revolution in land use involving a change in the whole relationship of communities to the land. Sometimes changes take place which affect only limited areas owing to some particular property they possess. The Cleveland District of Yorkshire is a case in point. By the end of 1852 the county of Yorkshire as a whole was provided with a fairly close mesh of railways, but, with the exception of the Whitby & Pickering line, no railway had as yet penetrated into the uplands of Cleveland and the North York Moors. The region was one of relatively sparse population and the terrain difficult enough to deter railway promoters in the absence of any particular attractions. Even the Railway Mania of the 'forties came and went with no tangible results in this district. But in 1850–1 the first discoveries of ironstone in the north-western extremity of the uplands were sowing the seeds of revolution and during the middle fifties there began the process which by 1885 had provided a network of lines much closer and more concentrated than in many a lowland where construction was easier and cheaper. A new requirement in the economic geography of Cleveland posed new demands and called into being an entirely new transport system.

A similar situation arose in the Rhondda valley, the upper part of which remained virtually undeveloped for some years after the penetration of other parts of the South Wales Coalfield by railways. When the short branch to Dinas (opened in 1841) was eventually extended to Treherbert in 1856[6] it made possible a vast development, which in turn encouraged the building of other railways, among them the Barry Railway, authorized in 1884. In both Cleveland and the Rhondda railways were both the cause

[6] D. S. Barrie, *The Taff Vale Railway* (1939), p. 12.

and the product of a major regional revolution, the marks of which may be seen in the present map.

Changes of this kind may be described as changes of situation in the geographical sense. The significance of a piece of country alters, and the equilibrium of the existing communications is disturbed, so that they are no longer adequate for the task demanded of them. This does not necessarily imply a diminution of the absolute efficiency of the prevailing system, but rather an increase in what is expected of it. It is one way in which communications may become obsolete. But obsolescence may also result if the techniques of communication are so improved as to set new standards which the established facilities cannot attain. It may well be that such changes correspond with changes of situation. The Roman roads in the Weald reflect a technical advance on their prehistoric counterparts as well as a change in regional situation. In the Industrial Revolution the two almost invariably went hand in hand, so that growing demands for transport in, say, the expanding coalfields were met by the provision of new and increasingly efficient kinds of communications. It is therefore often difficult and sometimes impossible to separate these two kinds of change, but the processes whereby the canals were displaced by the railways and, later, the rural branch railways were displaced by modern roads (and the associated bus services), clearly fall in the category of technical change.

Whatever the motive for adjustment in the pattern of communications, its implementation takes the form of adaptation where possible, replacement where not. The London to Yorkshire Motorway, for instance, does not use pre-existing communications at all. Indeed it deliberately avoids them and makes connexion with them only at infrequent intervals. The whole project has been conceived as a unit designed to achieve an objective (the fast and uninterrupted movement of long-distance traffic) for which the existing roads have proved themselves inadequate. It makes a calculated break with the method of adaptation which has hitherto brought into being practically all our network of roads. There have occasionally been periods, usually following the invention of new techniques, when entirely new elements of this sort were usual. The first canals, for instance, and many of the early railways, blazed entirely new trails. But once the rudiments of a network had been laid the tendency was for the existing parts to be used as a framework for further expansion.

There are several different ways in which adaptation can be said to have taken place. It may involve the technical improvement of existing communications, such as, for instance, in making rivers navigable. Although this may require the provision of artificial sections to eliminate obstacles or deviations, as has happened in the improvement of the rivers of South Yorkshire, it may merely take the form of dredging wider and deeper channels in the river. The extension of navigability on the Tyne as far as Ryton took this form. Or again modern railways have frequently been constructed by the improvement of earlier lines. The Sirhowy Railway, the Whitby & Pickering, and Canterbury & Whitstable and many others began life as wagonways for horse-drawn trains and were later converted and incorporated into the railway network. As far as the roads are concerned an overwhelming proportion of the present main roads represents adaptations of this kind.

Another kind of adaptation is that which involves a change of form from one mode of transport to another. Railway companies purchased canals and in a few instances converted them, either by filling in the channel or by using the canal bank for the railway. Hadfield mentions the Aberdeenshire, the Glastonbury, the Oakham, the Andover, and parts of the Leominster & Herefordshire and Gloucestershire Canals[7] as having been used in this way. The Gravesend–Strood railway follows the bank of the Thames & Medway Canal for some two miles east of Gravesend and from 1846[8] replaced the canal through the Strood Tunnel.

At the present time, when hundreds of miles of railway are falling into disuse, there is a strong prima facie case for applying to them similar processes of conversion, this time into roads. The radii of the curves of most railway lines would be an improvement on those of most main roads, though the curves on many branch lines would fail to measure up to the standards demanded by modern motorway engineers. Railway gradients would almost always be acceptable, even for motorways. The line of route would often be more direct than that of existing roads and would invariably afford either a by-pass for towns and villages or a clear passage through them independent of local traffic, except perhaps at level-crossings. The difficulties of land purchase would be largely overcome, and associated problems, such as those of farm access rights, would not arise, since they would already have

[7] C. Hadfield, *British Canals* (1950), p. 187.
[8] H. G. Lewin, *The Railway Mania and its Aftermath* (1936), p. 347.

been dealt with when the railway was built, neither would there be any question of taking over more land from agriculture. It is scarcely surprising, therefore, that numerous suggestions for converting railways into roads have been put forward all over the country.[9]

What is not generally realized, however, is that the width of a railway is very small compared with that of a road. Even a double-track line barely provides a width sufficient to accommodate a normal two-lane carriageway, which in any case would be far too narrow to make any real contribution to the solution of the road traffic problem. When it is remembered, too, that many if not most of the branch lines which are becoming available for this type of conversion are of single track, it will be understood that only in exceptional circumstances can one look for any useful measures of this kind, while the supposition that no further acquisition of land need be made turns out to be fallacious.

Exceptional circumstances, however, do exist, and occasionally the cost of conversion may be cheaper than the construction of an entirely new road. Current proposals provide for the incorporation of parts of the abandoned Merthyr & Abergavenny line in a trunk road from the Midlands to South Wales, and the possibilities of converting parts of the Monkland and Edinburgh Union Canals into modern roadways have also been discussed.[10] The Leek & Manifold Valley Railway has suffered conversion partly into a road and partly into a footpath.

The largest firm project of this kind yet put forward is that of the Norfolk County Council for the conversion of a nineteen-mile stretch of the disused Midland & Great Northern Joint Railway between Potter Heigham and Aylsham, but there is here a quite unusual combination of circumstances. In the first place the existing road-system is exceptionally bad for the purpose for which this new road is required. There is at present no first-class road leading westwards from Yarmouth and the Broads between the Norwich (A.47) and Cromer (A.149) roads and an increasing holiday traffic makes it imperative to provide one, while the existing second-class and minor roads are so sinuous that their conversion would be a very expensive undertaking. Secondly the planned road width is only 24 feet, so that, although it will be a very big improvement in this type of country and will undoubtedly relieve

[9] *The Engineer*, 31 Jan. 1958.
[10] *Report of the Committee of Inquiry into Inland Waterways* (1958), p. 63.

traffic congestion at peak periods, it would make very little impression on the sort of traffic problems which are habitually encountered in industrial areas. Thirdly the track lies through comparatively level country and is at or near the level of the surrounding land nearly all the way. There are some cuttings and embankments in the western half, but east of Honing there are virtually none. This is important, because the line was of single track throughout, except in the stations, and a considerable amount of lineside land will therefore have to be acquired to make up the required width, and the widening of cuttings and embankments would add greatly to the cost. It does not by any means follow, therefore, that what can be done here can necessarily be done elsewhere.

The adaptation of communications is frequently brought about by the provision of new parts which are so positioned as to improve or even alter the function of pre-existing sections. The conversion of pre-motor roads into modern first-class carriageways frequently involves such a process, and one cannot travel very far on the main roads of this country without finding remnants of roadway which have been eliminated by direct cuts. The process of straightening out roads in this way is actively proceeding all over the country at the present time. Comparable cut-offs often occur on the railways as part of the process of conversion from early and more primitive wagonways. The Old Hayle Railway, for instance, of 1834, was acquired by the West Cornwall Railway under its Act of Incorporation (1846), and, although parts of the track were converted to form the main line between Redruth and Hayle, two deviations were necessary to eliminate inclined planes.[11] A similar deviation was made for a similar reason at Goathland on the Whitby & Pickering. The same kind of thing happened on the canals. Particularly when they had been constructed to follow the contours, there was opportunity for shortening them by straighter, but necessarily costlier cuts. Hadfield[12] cites the Oxford Canal between Hillmorton and Hawkesbury as an example. Parts of the original canal together with the new cuts can be clearly seen from the train on the West Coast main line between Brinklow and Shilton stations (now closed). Further south a good example occurs at Wolfhampcote (Plate 31).

Cut-offs on this scale can really be regarded as improvements

[11] E. T. MacDermot, *History of the Great Western Railway*, vol. 2 (1931), p. 300.
[12] C. Hadfield, op. cit., p. 148.

Photo: J. K. St. Joseph, by permission of the Committee for Aerial
Photography, University of Cambridge, and of the Air Ministry
Crown Copyright Reserved

PLATE 31. ABANDONED CANAL, WOLFHAMPCOTE,
WARWICKSHIRE

The Oxford Canal, which, between Napton and Hillmorton, followed the contours on the south-eastern side of the Avon valley at 322 feet, encountered near Wolfhampcote one of its principal left-bank tributaries, the Leam.

In order to maintain the level without the expense of building a tall embankment, it was necessary to make a southward salient a mile or so up the Leam valley. The embankment was subsequently built, the salient eliminated and the route shortened. A section of the abandoned salient can be seen passing across part of the site of the deserted village of Wolfhampcote with its surrounding 'ridge-and-furrow'. The Weedon–Leamington railway and the former Great Central main line can be seen in the foreground and top left-hand corner respectively. View to the north-west.

in existing lines of communication. Sometimes, however, the provision of short sections in strategic places results in such important changes in the functions of existing stretches of line as virtually to constitute new routes. This process has played its part in the evolution of many main lines. All three recognized rail routes from London to Scotland afford examples, but perhaps the most interesting cut-offs of this kind are to be found on the former Great Western Railway, which towards the end of the century initiated a vigorous programme of cut-off building.[13] By the construction of some half-dozen short sections of new line and the reconstruction of parts of existing branches, great improvements were effected in the communications from Paddington. The South Wales & Bristol Direct Line, opened in 1903 from Wootton Bassett (six miles west of Swindon) to Patchway, on the line between Bristol and the Severn Tunnel, resulted in a saving of ten miles and kept the South Wales traffic off the busy stretch of line through Bath and the Box Tunnel. It represents a thirty-mile stretch of the present main line to Cardiff. By the opening of a new section between Old Oak Common and High Wycombe (1903–5), the rebuilding of the single-track line from there to Princes Risborough and an extension to Aynho (1910),[14] the Great Western route to Birmingham was reduced by $18\frac{1}{2}$ miles. But probably the most important of these cut-offs were the three short lengths necessary to open up the West of England main line. Up to this time the Great Western route to Exeter was via Didcot, Swindon, Bristol, and Bridgwater; indeed the company's initials were said to stand for the 'Great Way Round'. South of this the company possessed several branch lines which could be used to form the basis of a direct main line to Taunton. The various components of this potential route were as follows:

1. The Berks & Hants Railway of 1845, acquired by the Great Western in 1846 and opened in 1847 from Reading to Hungerford.

2. The Berks & Hants Extension line of 1859, opened in 1862 from Hungerford to Devizes.

3. The Wilts, Somerset & Weymouth Railway of 1845, opened from Chippenham to Westbury in 1848, Westbury to Frome in 1850, and Frome to Weymouth in 1856–7. (Acquired by the G.W.R. in 1850.)

4. The Yeovil Branch of the Bristol & Exeter Railway (amalgamated with the Great Western in 1876), authorized in 1845 and opened in 1853 from Durston, on the Bristol & Exeter main line six miles east of Taunton, to Yeovil.

There were therefore two main gaps to be bridged. The first was between Stert (Patney and Chirton) on the Berks & Hants Extension line to Westbury on the Wilts, Somerset & Weymouth. The second was from Castle Cary on the same line to a point

[13] Details based on MacDermot and Lewin, op. cit.
[14] Parts of the work being carried out jointly with the Great Central Railway.

known as Curry Rivel Junction near Langport on the Durston–
Yeovil Branch. Powers to span these two gaps had first been
obtained as early as 1848[15] and had subsequently been renewed
but no serious attempt to implement them was made until 1895.
The Stert–Westbury section was opened in 1900. The Castle Cary–
Curry Rivel section followed in 1905–6. The project involved also
the doubling of the Hungerford–Stert section and of the Yeovil
Branch west of Curry Rivel, and in order to improve the line still
further a third short cut was provided at the western end of the
branch, cutting out the junction at Durston Station and joining
the Bristol–Exeter line at Cogload.

This question of the adaptation of pre-existing elements in the
pattern raises another point, namely that the various parts may
themselves have had quite different characteristics which render
them of more or of less value as the raw material of a later network
of communications. Some can be more easily adapted than others.
Consider, for instance, the present road-system of the Scottish
Highlands. In tracing its ancestry one would encounter roads of
many different origins. Let us briefly examine three kinds.

The Highland drove-roads were little more than recognized
rights of way through the mountains.

> In the main [says Haldane] it seems clear that during much of the
> droving period and over great stretches of the Highlands the droves
> moved as they chose through a country unmarked by tracks other
> than their own. . . . Droving traffic was in general unrestricted, free
> to cross a wide area or to change its route according to the weather, the
> season, or the many other factors which influenced that uncertain
> trade.[16]

It is probably only in their general direction and geographical
situation that we are justified in regarding these drove-roads as
the ancestors of our present motorways. They are sufficiently
clearly defined for Haldane to have mapped them on a scale of
about ten miles to the inch, but 'the identification on the ground
of the actual line of march is in many cases a matter of great
difficulty'.[17]

By comparison the military roads of the eighteenth century
resembled much more closely a modern road. The earliest of these
were built by General Wade in the late seventeen-twenties and
early 'thirties. They were much more than mere tracks. They were

[15] H. G. Lewin, op. cit., p. 370.
[16] A. R. B. Haldane, *The Drove Roads of Scotland* (1952), pp. 31–32.
[17] ibid., p. 32.

constructed to planned measurements (generally 16 feet in width), they crossed rivers by new bridges and in places the rock had to be blasted away to make room for them. According to Mathieson 'the Roman method of making roads in a series of straight lines was adopted, knolls and moors being crossed without considering steep gradients or mossy bogs'.[18] Whether or not this is a fair description of Roman methods, it is clear from the courses of the Wade roads that they did not make the most advantageous use of the opportunities afforded by the land-surface. Gibb[19] quotes Southey as saying that Wade followed the horse leads, 'instead of surveying the country like an engineer', and although the poet may not have spoken with the authority of a surveyor, Gibb regards his opinions as reflecting those of Telford in whose company he had just completed a highland tour. Rolt[20] also suggests that Telford had no high opinion of Wade as an engineer.

It is not surprising, therefore, that the Wade roads have only occasionally proved suitable for direct adaptation to modern needs. Apart from those sections which have been totally abandoned and are not even approximately followed by modern roads (such as the Dalwhinnie–Fort Augustus road, over the 2,500-foot pass of Corrie Yairack, and the Tummel Bridge–Dalnacardoch road further south), the Wade roads can often be seen as derelict tracks parallel with and at some little distance from the present road. The Dunkeld–Inverness road, for instance (A.9), 'deviates in many places from the Wade road'.[21] At the southern end the Duke of Atholl 'greatly improved the military road from Dunkeld to Blair Atholl, changing the direction in many places to avoid pulls'[22] (Plate 8).

The roads surveyed by Telford, Donaldson, and others for the Commissioners for Highland Roads and Bridges in the years following the Act of 1803 also tended to follow approximately the old drove-roads, as for instance between Fort William and Arisaig or along the east coast beyond Dingwall. But this is country of strong relief, and the opportunities for communication were so limited and so closely related to physiography that it would have been remarkable if there had been no such correspondence. These roads, however, were more methodically engineered than the

---

[18] J. Mathieson, 'General Wade and his military roads in the Highlands of Scotland'. *S.G.M.* 40 (1924), p. 196.
[19] Sir Alexander Gibb, *The Story of Thomas Telford* (1935), p. 160.
[20] L. T. C. Rolt, *Thomas Telford* (1958), p. 63.
[21] Mathieson, op. cit., p. 201.   [22] ibid., p. 211.

military roads of General Wade, and they have usually proved
more suitable for adaptation to modern requirements. Most of
the road-building of this period was undertaken in the North-
West Highlands beyond the Great Glen, and in this area Telford
and his associates can be said to have laid the foundations of the
present road-system in a more precise sense than ever Wade could
claim to have done in the Grampians.

From these three examples, then, the drove-roads, the Wade
roads, and the Commissioners' roads, it becomes clear that the
different functions of these earlier 'ancestral' roads are reflected
in different degrees of suitability for adaptation to later needs.
It is not merely a question of date but of purpose as well. The
Wade roads were no improvement on the drove-roads for purposes
of droving, a fact which kept many of the drove-roads in use long
after the construction of highways which were technically superior
from every other point of view.[23] And although these Wade roads
in turn ushered in a revolution in Highland road-building, they
did not go far enough to make themselves acceptable as modern
roads, whereas the Commissioners' roads, being closer to modern
requirements not only in date but in their technical properties,
have more frequently been followed by their successors in the
details of their position and not merely in their general direction.

A tremendous opportunity for wholesale adaptation arose in
the eighteenth and early nineteenth centuries in thousands of
English parishes when their open fields were enclosed. Tracts of
land which for centuries had been farmed by one method were
re-allocated on an entirely different basis. In this re-allocation
the pre-existing roads might or might not conveniently fit into the
new schemes. The Commissioners of Inclosure appointed to carry
out the transition, frequently favoured straight roads of regular
widths, often 40 or 60 feet. Sometimes these roads followed the line
of earlier tracks, but sometimes new roads were laid out where no
previous thoroughfare had existed. The Bridlington Road at
Speeton, Yorkshire, is a good example (Plate 32). Neville's map
of 1772 in the East Riding Record Office shows the open arable
fields of Speeton spread out to the south of the village, with no
road in this direction. The complete rearrangement of land use
in the parish under the Inclosure Award of 1794 provided the
opportunity to make one, approximately, but not exactly, along
the boundary between two of the earlier open fields.

[23] For an English example see Hoskins on Sewston Lane, op. cit., p. 189.

Photo: Brian Fisher

PLATE 32. BRIDLINGTON ROAD, SPEETON, YORKSHIRE

An 'Inclosure' road dating from 1794. Note the straightness of the road and the width of its verges. At its far end it enters the Reighton–Flamborough road by a 'T-junction'.

To reach the village centre (seen beyond the 'T-junction') traffic has to make two right-angle turns because the direct line of approach lay across land already enclosed in 1794. The level-crossing carries the Scarborough–Bridlington railway. View to the north.

Another way in which one can examine the geographical implications of the process of 'growth by adaptation' is by looking at some examples of the kind of detail which one finds in the present map but which cannot be explained in terms of present function. For instance, the one-inch map[24] shows an apparently anomalous situation at Cockermouth (Cumberland), where the line from Workington suddenly changes from double to single track (Fig. 23A). Had the change taken place in Cockermouth Station one might have inferred that a greater volume of traffic between Cockermouth and the coast necessitated the duplication of the track in this section, but in fact the change takes place some three-quarters of a mile west of the station, so that the advantage

[24] O.S. 1-inch map, sheet 82.

of the extra line capacity would seem to be lost in the bottleneck which this short length of single-track line interposes. Neither is there any physical obstacle to suggest an explanation, as in the examples of the Malvern and Ledbury tunnels or the Saltash Bridge (see Chapter V). In fact the double-track line is part of the original Cockermouth & Workington Railway which was opened in 1847 to a terminus adjacent to the River Derwent on the western side of the town. The single-track line is that of the former Cockermouth, Keswick & Penrith Railway, opened in 1865, and the present station is situated on this line at the point where it passes closest to the town centre. The actual terminus of the line, however, is where it makes contact with the Cockermouth & Workington, and the change from double to single track marks the junction between what were once the lines of two separate companies, opened at different dates.

This is a simple example of what happened time and again in the urban geography of Britain. A terminal line built into the town could not be extended beyond the original terminal point because the town centre blocked the way. The continuation-line had therefore to be taken out of the existing railway at some point short of the terminal station, and carried round the town centre. The original terminus was then frequently supplanted by a new through station and was generally taken over for use as a goods station. Curzon Street Station, the original terminus in Birmingham, suffered such a fate by the building of the New Street extension authorized in 1846, though this can hardly be said to have avoided the town centre, except by passing underneath it. A better example would be seen in Manchester. Here the sites of the original termini of the Liverpool & Manchester (Liverpool Road) and Manchester & Leeds (Oldham Road) are still occupied by goods stations, but passenger traffic has for over a century been dealt with at Victoria and (later) Exchange stations on the through line provided round the northern side of the city centre.

Similar examples of goods stations (not necessarily the original buildings) performing functions for which they were not originally constructed, but to which they were relegated when passenger traffic found better accommodation, may be seen in very many towns. A few examples will have to suffice. In Hull the original terminus of the Hull & Selby was on the site of the present goods station adjacent to the Humber Dock and was replaced by Paragon Station in 1848. Much later (1924) the Hull & Barnsley terminus (Cannon Street) suffered a similar fate.[25] The site of the terminus of the Lancaster & Preston Junction Railway in Lancaster can easily be detected on the one-inch map,[26] since it is approached by an almost straight continuation of the main line from the south, whereas the present main line northwards towards Carlisle (Lancaster & Carlisle Railway of 1844) swings sharply out of alignment at Lancaster Old Junction to pass through the present (Castle) Station. In Leeds goods stations are still in operation on the sites of the Marsh Lane and Hunslet Lane termini of the Hull & Selby and North Midland Railways respectively. In Leicester the West Bridge terminus of the Leicester & Swannington Railway was left in isolation by the opening in 1849 of the section from Desford to the Midland main line at Knighton, which enabled passenger services to use the Midland (London Road) station. In Newcastle-on-Tyne goods stations at Forth Banks, Manors, and New Bridge Street occupy the sites of the earlier termini of the Newcastle & Carlisle, Newcastle & North Shields, and Blyth & Tyne Railways respectively. Harrogate, Newport (Monmouthshire), Preston, Salisbury, Sheffield, and Truro are among other towns where such a feature can easily be distinguished.

All these examples illustrate communications which, having been completed to discharge some particular and generally local function, had to be adapted and assimilated into a changing network. More curious are those schemes which for one reason or another attained only partial completion in their original intended form. The finished sections came into operation but necessarily in a capacity quite different from that for which they were designed.

During the late eighteen-fifties two small companies were engaged in building a railway along the upper part of the Severn valley from Welshpool to Llanidloes (Fig. 28), and this was completed by June 1861.[27] Beyond Llanidloes the Mid Wales Railway was to extend this line over into the Wye valley in the direction of Rhayader and Newbridge. Meanwhile to the south-west a small network of lines was emerging in Pembrokeshire, based on the South Wales Railway, from which another company, the Carmarthen & Cardigan, had been authorized, since 1854, to build a line northwards from Carmarthen to the Teifi valley at Llan-

[25] G. D. Parkes, *The Hull & Barnsley Railway* (1946), p. 12.
[26] O.S. 1-inch map, sheet 89.
[27] E. T. MacDermot, op. cit., vol. 2, p. 437.

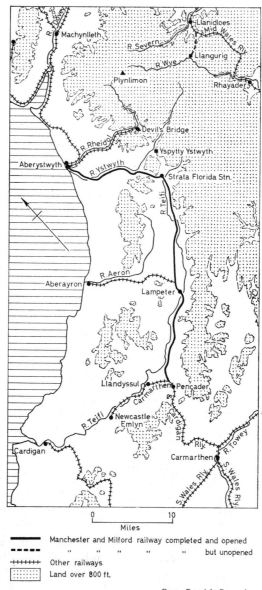

Crown Copyright Reserved

FIG. 28. THE MANCHESTER & MILFORD RAILWAY,
CENTRAL WALES

Based on details from E. T. MacDermot, 'History of the Great Western Railway'

dussyl and on to Newcastle Emlyn, though it took some ten years
to reach the Teifi. As this line approached the Teifi it made a
right-angle bend westward at Pencader, from which point, or
just beyond it, the upper part of the Teifi valley continued north-
eastward about two-thirds of the way to, and in a direct line with,
Llanidloes. Beyond the headwaters of the Teifi, however, there
lay a more difficult piece of country in which the Ystwyth and
Rheidol, flowing west to the sea, had excavated deep valleys, and
between these and the Severn at Llanidloes was interposed a part
of yet another drainage-system—the upper Wye.

In 1860 a company was authorized to connect the Carmarthen
& Cardigan at Pencader with the Mid Wales Railway just south
of Llanidloes, following the upper Teifi and then passing through
this difficult country by way of Yspytty Ystwyth, Devil's Bridge,
and the col on the southern side of Plynlimon. The final crossing
between Wye and Severn drainage was to be made by the pass
east of Llangurig. The objective behind the scheme[28] is suggested
by the company's pretentious title, The Manchester & Milford
Railway. Its finances were quite inadequate, but it did succeed
in completing the southern portion from Pencader to Strata
Florida Station, which was opened in two stages in 1866. Already,
however, it had become apparent that the completion of the more
difficult part to Llanidloes was impossible with the available
funds, and in 1865 an Act had been obtained to continue the line
from Strata Florida down the Ystwyth valley to Aberystwyth.
This was opened in 1867, and the remainder abandoned. The
function of the line was therefore very different from what had
been conceived, and its shape on the map, with the sharp change
of direction at Strata Florida, is a monument to the unhappy
history of its origin. To complete the picture one may look at the
one-inch map[29] where one will find, flanking the main road
(A.492) between Llangurig and Llanidloes, an 'Abandoned Railway', the north-eastern extremity of the Manchester & Milford,
which having been completed in 1863, was never opened.[30]

When a scheme included sharply contrasting sections of line,
one part being easy to construct, the other difficult, there were
two possible ways of embarking on its construction. From one
point of view it was desirable to bring into operation at least a

[28] E. G. Bowen, *Wales: a Physical, Historical and Regional Geography* (1957), pp. 223–4.
[29] O.S. 1-inch map, sheet 128, New Popular Edition (1947). On the Seventh Series
sheet (1952) it is not shown.
[30] E. T. MacDermot, op. cit., vol. 2, p. 439.

part of the line as soon as possible, so that it could be earning revenue while the remainder was being completed. The other school of thought argued that it was better to begin with the more difficult parts, which would take longer to construct, so that the whole could be finished as soon as possible. An *ad hoc* decision as to which method was preferable had to be made in every case in the light of potential traffic, construction costs, etc. The Manchester & Milford clearly inclined to the former view as did the Great Northern Railway of 1846, which put all its efforts into completing the Peterborough–Boston–Lincoln loop before its main line, which was authorized at the same time, on the grounds that it could be more easily undertaken.[31] But sometimes other counsels prevailed, as in the case of the direct line between York and Leeds, also of 1846, in which the fine masonry viaduct over the Wharfe at Tadcaster was commenced immediately, as being in all probability the part which would take longest to complete. In the event it was virtually the only part of the scheme to be finished.

One of the most interesting and curious examples of an uncompleted system is to be found in the former Ellesmere Canal, which later became a part of the Shropshire Union. Its only connexion with the main canal system was at Hurleston, near Nantwich, from which point it ran south-west, throwing out branches to Whitchurch, Edstaston (near Prees), and Weston, this last terminating among the fields some nine miles north-west of Shrewsbury. From Frankton one line continued to Llanymynech and there connected with the Montgomeryshire Canal. The other branched north-west, passed over two of the largest aqueducts in Britain, only to stop short immediately at Cefn-Mawr, just as it seemed about to penetrate the Wrexham Coalfield. From the aqueduct head also a long arm swung west away from the coalfield to Llangollen (Fig. 29).

This paradoxical layout defies explanation in terms of economic geography. Only its evolution gives a clue. The main line of the canal, authorized in 1793, was to pass from Chester through the Wrexham Coalfield to the Severn at Shrewsbury with various branches, and a continuation was provided northwards across the Wirral to the Mersey at a place to which it gave the name of Ellesmere Port. The company concentrated at once on the completion of this easy section and it was opened in 1795. This done,

---

[31] C. H. Grinling, *The History of the Great Northern Railway* (1898), pp. 63–64.

however, they adopted the opposite view with regard to the main line, namely that the more difficult section should be undertaken first. This lay just to the south of the Wrexham Coalfield through

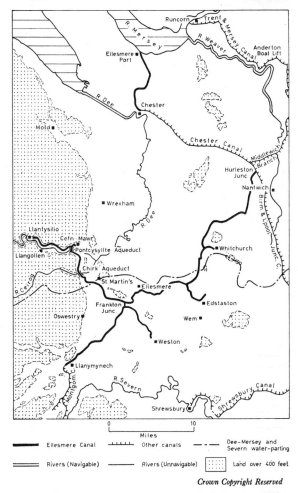

FIG. 29. THE ELLESMERE CANAL

which the canal was to pass at a height of a little more than 300 feet, that is to say at the same altitude as the watershed between Dee and Severn drainage which it had to cross near St. Martin's some ten miles further south. It was therefore most desirable to maintain the canal above the 300-foot contour until this watershed had been reached, a task which necessitated the

G.C.—M

building of the two aqueducts in question, at Pontcysyllte and Chirk, where the deeply cut valleys of the Dee and its tributary the Ceiriog respectively lay across the path of the canal.

Here again the company's financial resources were inadequate, and the line as completed represented only a truncated portion of the scheme originally planned, starting at Cefn-Mawr and running to Weston Wharf. Fortunately, it was found practicable to alter the proposed Whitchurch Branch and make a continuation to the Chester Canal at Hurleston, which is how it came about that what started as a branch became the main line and vice versa, and why the resulting pattern seems at first sight to be so incongruous. The Llangollen branch, incidentally, was technically necessary as the main feeder to the canal. This had to run up the Dee valley to a point (Llantysilio) where the river was higher than the summit section of the canal, and it was not much trouble to make it navigable at the same time.

In all these examples financial miscalculations were responsible for changes in plan during construction, and, although its manifestations were not usually so spectacular, the money-market always exerted a controlling influence on the development of communications. It illustrates clearly enough the way in which ephemeral conditions can leave behind permanent traces. The timing of the great phases of expansion of canals and railways was related to the ready availability of money for investment just as the meagre programme of post-war road-construction was a product of financial stringency. O'Dell brings this out in a reference to the Midland Railway extension from Leicester to Bedford 'which was constructed during the Crimean War and, without adequate finances, the route included the Desborough Bank with four miles of 1 in 50. Later the company avoided this incubus by a deviation line with better gradients.' [32]

Many features of the present map of communications arise from the fact that they came into existence against a background of competition. This can be most clearly seen in the railways, though turnpike roads and canals furnish examples. The most important consequence of competition in the spread of the railway network was the incentive which it provided for companies to extend their lines into distant regions already served by their rivals, often with the result that duplicate lines were constructed. Duplicate lines of this kind can be seen in the Avon valley below Bath, between

[32] A. C. O'Dell, *Railways and Geography* (1956), p. 35.

Croydon and Redhill, in many of the valleys of the South Wales Coalfield (Plate 23), in the Rother valley below Chesterfield, between Neilston (Renfrewshire) and Barrmill (Ayrshire), to take a few random examples. Perhaps the best is in the Leen valley (Nottinghamshire). Here, for some ten miles, three railways run north from the outskirts of Nottingham to Annesley. Nowhere are they as much as three-quarters of a mile apart. They can be explained only in terms of the climate of competition which prevailed in the nineteenth century. But this competition was not merely a local matter concerned with the traffic of the valley itself. It grew out of a much wider struggle which was being waged on a much larger field, as large as the whole railway map of Britain. The first line, that of the Midland Railway, was opened in 1848–9 as a branch line from Nottingham to Mansfield.[33] The second line did aim exclusively at the local traffic of this important coal-mining valley. It was opened by the Great Northern in 1881 as a terminal branch. But even this was an essential part of the much larger plan by which the company sought to break the near-monopoly of the Midland Railway in the Derbyshire–Nottinghamshire Coalfield.[34] The third line was quite different in concept. It was built in the 'nineties parallel with the other two railways chiefly because the Leen valley happened to lend itself to the ambitious scheme by which the Manchester, Sheffield & Lincolnshire Railway, hitherto confined to the North of England, built itself a main line to London.[35] To the Midland Railway the valley appeared as profitable territory on the way to Mansfield. To the Great Northern it appeared as a rich coal-producing area in rival hands. To the M.S. & L. its physiographic importance as a routeway giving access to Nottingham and eventually to Marylebone was paramount.

Competition between different companies has also been the primary cause of the construction of more than one station in a town, though it is not the only reason.[36] Consequently multiplicity of stations is a particularly common feature in those areas where competition was rife; it is much less usual where one company succeeded in establishing a monopoly or near-monopoly at an

[33] H. G. Lewin, op. cit., pp. 170 and 391.
[34] C. H. Grinling, op. cit., pp. 256–7, 339, and 247–8.
[35] ibid., Chapter XXIV.
[36] In Falkirk, for instance, differences in altitude between the Edinburgh–Glasgow and the Polmont–Larbert lines were responsible for the provision of two stations by the same company.

early date. Thus there are at least two principal stations in many of the towns of the Midlands, such as Birmingham, Wolverhampton, Derby, Leicester, Loughborough, Nottingham, Rugby, Nuneaton, Peterborough, and even smaller places like Thrapston, Stamford, and Rugeley. In Liverpool there are three, in Manchester no less than five. By contrast the territory of the former North-Eastern Railway has practically no duplication of town stations (except for suburban stations, which is a different matter). It seems to have been the policy of the North-Eastern Board to aim at establishing a monopoly in Northumberland, Durham, and the North and East Ridings of Yorkshire, and in this area even large towns like Middlesbrough, York, Newcastle, Sunderland, Darlington, and West Hartlepool handle all their traffic in single central stations, though in many of them, such as Newcastle, Durham, and Stockton, traces of two or more stations bear witness to a vigorous competition in earlier days.

Hand-in-hand with competition goes its opposite—co-operation, which had quite a different influence on the emerging network. Generally speaking railway companies found themselves in competition with each other when they both owned lines between the same places. Where, however, their properties lay, not parallel, but end-to-end, the position was very different, since the one tended to act as a feeder to the other. However much effort a company made to cultivate traffic within its own territory it had to rely on other companies for traffic emanating beyond its own extremities. All manner of devices were used to further the interests of companies in this way, including traffic agreements, working agreements, leases, the exercise of running powers over other companies' track, amalgamations, purchases, and the promotion of extensions. These extensions might take the form of branches from the main system, or, as often happened, they might be promoted by nominally independent companies which were to pass under the control of the parent company on, or sometimes before, completion.

This was the normal way in which the trunk lines of Britain were built. Only five times did any one company build one continuous stretch of line more than a hundred miles in length under the authority of a single Act of Parliament.[37] This piecemeal

[37] Ignoring minor deviations authorized during construction, this was achieved by the London & Birmingham (1833), the Great Western (Paddington–Bristol, 1835), the South Wales Railway (1845), the Great Northern (King's Cross–Shaftholme, 1846), and the Inverness & Perth Junction (Dunkeld–Forres, 1861). The West Highland Railway (Craigendoran–Fort William, 1889) was about a furlong short of 100 miles.

development of trunk lines is well illustrated by the present route of the Cornish Riviera Express. It includes the three short sections previously described, and is shown in Figure 30.

A comparable analysis of other main lines would reveal the same sort of result. A Euston–Aberdeen express, for instance,

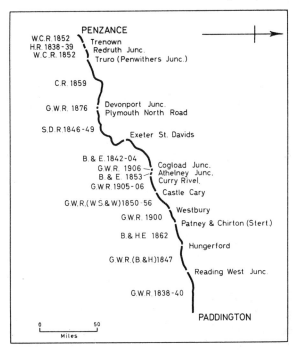

Fig. 30. THE EVOLUTION OF THE MAIN LINE OF THE FORMER G.W.R. FROM PADDINGTON TO PENZANCE

B. & E., Bristol & Exeter; B. & H., Berks & Hants; B. & H.E., Berks & Hants Extension; C.R., Cornwall Rly.; S.D.R., South Devon Rly.; W.C.R., West Cornwall Rly.; W.S. & W., Wilts, Somerset & Weymouth. The section between Redruth Junction and Trenowin (Hayle Rly.) includes the Penponds Deviation, built by the W.C.R.

Based on details from E. T. MacDermot, 'History of the Great Western Railway'

would pass over railways originally built by at least sixteen different companies. The provision of short cuts, such as that between Winwick Junction and Golborne Junction (Lancashire) which is comparable with, say, the Athelney–Cogload cut-off, represents one element in the picture of a gradual build-up of through routes from smaller parts. Or again both the Penzance and Aberdeen lines just quoted contain fragments of early mineral railways, the Hayle Railway in Cornwall, the Wishaw & Coltness and the Monkland & Kirkintilloch Railways in Scotland.

It is easy to see how this kind of growth has given rise to the popular misconception that the origin of all trunk lines, which are the product of the fusion of smaller units, is a haphazard affair. Financial limitations frequently led railway companies in the early period to restrict their activities to comparatively local projects. But very often they laid out their track with the specific objective of making end-on junctions with other companies' lines. Often they employed the same engineer. Brunel, for instance, was engineer to the Great Western, Bristol & Exeter, South Devon, and Cornwall Railways, which between them provided the original route (via Bristol) from Paddington as far as Truro. Again, although the gap between the London & Birmingham Railway at Rugby and the Stockton & Darlington at Croft on the Tees was bridged by four separate companies, all of them received their authority within the two Sessions of 1836 and 1837. There was nothing fortuitous about this.

The evolution of a network of communications, therefore, must be seen against a background of constant change. It is not safe to suppose that similarities of form always indicate similarities of origin. While one may safely dismiss the possibility of a broad, straight road being a medieval creation, it is less easy to say from its appearance alone whether it was first laid out by Roman engineers or Commissioners of Inclosure. But whatever the form of communication, whatever the present function, whatever the period of its inception, a meaningful interpretation of its significance in the landscape will more often than not demand some investigation of its ancestry.

CHAPTER VII

NODES AND JUNCTIONS

The words 'node' and 'junction' are both used to describe points of convergence of lines of communication, but whereas 'junction' implies merely a joining-up, 'node' suggests a property which may exist in varying degrees and is related to the 'accessibility' of a place from its surrounding area. The adjectival form 'nodal' is used of places which possess this property of 'nodality'. Norwich (Fig. 20) has a very high degree of nodality. So has Crewe, but only in its railway system. The word 'accessibility' has recently been used in a more restricted sense, in which it refers to the availability of public passenger services connecting urban centres with the rural areas which they serve, and the Ordnance Survey has published a map of Great Britain[1] which aims to show this.

Clearly there is a relationship between the size of a town (as measured by its population) and its nodality, larger towns tending to exhibit this property more than smaller ones, but when one comes to look at particular examples, one finds that this criterion is only one of several. Bracey,[2] Green, Dickinson, Smailes, and others have devised and applied methods whereby the relative status of towns and cities as service-centres for their surrounding areas can be measured. In all assessments of this sort communications play an essential part and indeed represent the machinery by which a town asserts its influence over its 'urban field'. But tempting as it is to pursue this aspect of the subject it would lead into too wide a discussion. In any case one could do no more than 'pot' the published literature which is becoming comparatively abundant. Furthermore, while there is most certainly a close

---

[1] Local Accessibility (*The Hinterlands of Towns and Other Centres as determined by an Analysis of Bus Services*), 1/625,000, Ordnance Survey (1955).

[2] The following will give an introductory idea of the methods used:

H. E. Bracey, 'Towns as rural service-centres—an index of centrality with special reference to Somerset'. *I.B.G., Trans. & Papers*, 19 (1953), p. 95.

F. H. W. Green, 'Urban Hinterlands in England and Wales. An analysis of bus services'. *G.J.*, cxvi (1950), p. 64.

R. E. Dickinson, 'The regional functions and zones of influence of Leeds and Bradford'. *Geography*, xv (1929–30), p. 548.

A. E. Smailes, 'The analysis and delimitation of urban fields'. *Geography*, xxxii (1947), p. 151.

A. E. Smailes, *The Geography of Towns* (1953), Chapter VII.

relationship between accessibility as measured by the availability of public transport services and nodality as measured by the availability of actual lines of communication, the two concepts are, in fact, different, and it is with the latter that we are here concerned.

First, therefore, one must enquire how this property of nodality is to be found in different degrees in different places, and the most important aspect of the whole question is that of scale. The extreme example is London. Nowhere else in Britain (and perhaps the world) does one find quite the same degree of concentration of lines of communication on a focal centre. The pattern of roads and railways throughout the whole of south-eastern England is dominated by it. Certainly several factors have played their part in developing it. The growth of numerous small and medium-sized towns along the coast from Bournemouth to the Thames, each supporting direct links with the capital, has been important. So has the absence, apart from ferries, of any vehicular crossing of the Thames below the Blackwall Tunnel. So has the dearth of any really large towns which could rival it. Outside Greater London there are no cities south-east of the Oxford Clay Vale with populations as large as a quarter of a million and only ten of over 100,000.[3] Functionally London stands in a class by itself.[4] Indeed it is so large that the focal point in the centre has grown to a focal zone. The process of extreme concentration has begun to be relaxed and, paradoxically, its sheer size has, in a precise interpretation, brought about a lessening of its nodality. The principal railway termini, for instance, are mostly located on the fringe of the central core. It is as though the spokes of the wheel had been chopped off before they reached the hub. In the road-system, too, the radial elements become more difficult to trace as one approaches the centre. Subsidiary *foci* can be recognized in the street-plan, such as at Marble Arch, Hyde Park Corner, and the Elephant and Castle. On historical grounds one could, perhaps, identify a centre somewhere in the City, but it could only rank today as one of several. For well over a century it has been quite usual to calculate mileages for purposes of itineraries, etc., from Hyde

---

[3] Counting Rochester, Chatham, and Gillingham as a single urban unit (population 158,938). The others (1951 Census) are Portsmouth (233,464), Southampton (178,326), Brighton (156,440), Southend (151,830), Bournemouth (144,726), Norwich (121,226), Reading (114,176), Luton (110,370), and Ipswich (104,788).

[4] A. E. Smailes, 'The Urban Hierarchy in England and Wales'. *Geography*, xxix (1944), p. 41.

Park Corner, which is some three miles from the Mansion House.[5]
Again, traffic for different parts of London may be separated far
out in the country. For instance, at Pampisford Fork, Cambridge-
shire, some fifty-five miles from London, traffic from Norwich is
directed alternatively along A.11 to London via Epping or along
A.505 to London via Ware. Traffic for the docks goes by A.11 but
much traffic for the West End takes the other fork. On the Great
North Road a similar separation takes place at Alconbury Hill,
Huntingdonshire, as much as seventy miles out.

The railways, too, show comparable features. Electric trains
from Watford, for instance, are separated at Chalk Farm, some
running to Euston, some to Broad Street. Traffic from the Chatham line divides for Victoria and Holborn Viaduct at Herne Hill,
while the division of the Brighton line trains as between Victoria
and London Bridge takes place at Windmill Bridge Junction some
ten miles out. Charing Cross and Cannon Street afford another
example. In these cases the traffic of the City and of the West End
is sufficiently distinctive to affect profoundly the pattern of
services run over these lines. Cannon Street, Broad Street, and
Holborn Viaduct handle the bulk of their traffic in the rush hour,
whereas services to Victoria and Charing Cross, though certainly
exhibiting a peak load at the same times, are more evenly maintained throughout the day. In fact the separation of incoming
traffic is based on a functional difference between the parts of
London to which it flows.

There are few cities in Britain large enough for passenger rail
traffic to be divided for separate destinations in parts of the town
which are functionally different. Generally passenger termini are
situated as near to the town centre as the availability of a site
will permit, but separation of incoming trains does take place as
between different types of traffic. Goods traffic, for instance, may
be separated from passenger traffic as it approaches a town. This
happens at Trowse Upper Junction (Norwich), where traffic for
the goods terminus (Victoria) is separated from traffic for the
passenger terminus (Thorpe). It happens again at Roath Branch
Junction (Llandaff), where central traffic entering Cardiff from
the Taff Vale is separated from dock traffic. In Manchester
passenger traffic from Sheffield is separated at Guide Bridge, and
here the basis of discrimination is whether or not traffic is going
through to Liverpool. Both London Road and Central Stations

[5] The Automobile Association bases its calculations on Charing Cross.

in Manchester are situated fairly centrally. From Guide Bridge the approach to Central Station involves a wide sweep through the southern suburbs of Manchester and is more than six miles longer than the approach to London Road, which is therefore the usual station for trains terminating in Manchester. But trains which are due to run through to Liverpool are diverted from Guide Bridge to Central Station so as to enable them to proceed straight out along the Liverpool line. A similar facing junction for traffic approaching Manchester is to be found on the Crewe line at Wilmslow. Trains can be routed via Stockport or Styal, the decision being mainly a question of operating convenience, but in this case the lines converge again at Slade Lane Junction and both routes terminate in the same station (formerly called London Road, now Piccadilly).

There are, then, several reasons why some kinds of traffic on approaching large towns may be separated along different channels, even when their destinations lie within the town itself. Clearly all kinds of by-pass or avoiding-line add to this feature of separation. As a consequence there are always in the street-plans, and often in the railway layouts of towns, some divergent elements to counteract the dominant figures of converging lines, but generally speaking these divergent elements are more important in larger towns.

While the existence of a pattern of converging lines of road and railway is in itself an indication of nodality, there may be important functional contrasts between nodal centres which at first sight appear similar, and here again the question of scale is important. For instance, two of the largest nodal centres in the North of England are to be found in Newcastle and Carlisle, and, both as road and railway centres, one is tempted to see them as fulfilling equivalent functions on the East and West Coast routes respectively between England and Scotland. Each is the centre of a converging system of roads and railways with the main lines to Scotland forming a central axis. Each is a bridgehead, though the Tyne is crossed further downstream by numerous ferries (and by a pedestrian tunnel) while the Solway was at one time spanned by a railway viaduct. In the railway timetable the proportion of Anglo-Scottish express trains stopping at each is closely comparable, and in both cases the whole of the passenger traffic, with a very minor exception in Newcastle, is concentrated in a single central station. But in many ways the comparison breaks down as a result of two fundamental differences. The first is that the Solway penetrates far more deeply into the West Coast than does the Tyne into the East Coast, so that a straight line joining the gravity-centres of population in mid-Scotland and in Lancashire and Yorkshire would pass through Carlisle, whereas Newcastle is displaced fifty miles to the east of it. The second is that the Tyne

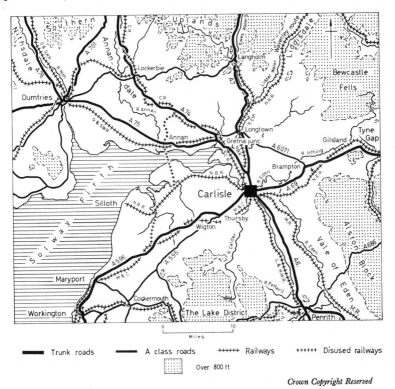

FIG. 31. THE COMMUNICATIONS OF THE CARLISLE BASIN

crossing at Newcastle is *locally* situated within an area of intense industrial development, whereas Carlisle is a comparatively small urban unit set in a rural matrix.

Carlisle, in short, owes everything to its situation, both on a national, and on a more restricted regional scale. Its immediate environment takes the form of a local structural basin lying between the Southern Uplands, the Lake District Dome, the Alston Block, and the Bewcastle Fells (Fig. 31). If the outcrop of the newest strata (the Lias) is taken as marking the centre of this basin, Carlisle is situated only some five miles from it. To the south-east the lowland is extended in a finger-like projection which is floored by New Red rocks stretching south to Appleby and Kirkby Stephen and which forms the Vale of Eden. The drainage of the whole area is markedly concentrated into the centre of the basin, and from a brief catalogue of the river-valleys concerned, taken in an anti-clockwise direction, their influence on the nodality of Carlisle is apparent. From the south the Calder is comparatively unimportant in so far as it gives access only to the sparsely in-habited fells on the northern side of the Lake District. But in the city it comes into its own, and where it threads its way along the western side of the old citadel its valley has become the focal centre of the railway system. The Petteril brings in the main railway and road (A.6) from Penrith and the South. The Eden valley brings the main line (Settle & Carlisle) from Leeds and St. Pancras. In the eastern sector the numerous rivers are mostly short and of steep profile as they run off the Carboniferous on to the Triassic rocks of the Basin. They tend therefore to be unsuit-able for communications, but the Irthing, with its abandoned tributary valley at Gilsland (the so-called 'Tyne Gap'), has deter-mined the course of the Newcastle and Carlisle line. Liddisdale carries the former North British ('Waverley Route') from Edin-burgh. The Esk, and its tributary the Ewes Water, provide a passage for the Carlisle–Edinburgh road (A.7). From the north-west Annandale brings the former Caledonian main line and the Glasgow road (A.74), Nithsdale the former Glasgow & South Western Railway and the road to the Ayrshire Coalfield (A.76). Finally nature has provided broad strips of comparative lowland on either side of the Solway, and of these the more northerly is used by the road and railway to south-west Scotland (and Northern Ireland via Stranraer), while the more southerly is the gateway to the West Cumberland Coalfield, carrying the Mary-port & Carlisle Railway, the Silloth Branch, and the A.595 road.

The nodality of Carlisle, therefore, has been enormously encouraged but not created by the physiography of its own basin. Economically the valleys concerned contribute a traffic which is small in comparison with that originating further afield. The position is emphasized by the fact that, of the 'A' roads converging on the city, all are Ministry of Transport trunk roads except one (A.595) and this stops short of the city, merging with the Mary-port trunk road (A.596) at Thursby, some four miles outside the city boundary. There is very little in the road-pattern of Carlisle intermediate between the national arterial roads and the local roads connecting up the city with the surrounding villages.

The railway system, too, is essentially related to the national trunk system. Before the grouping of 1923 no less than six separate companies reached the city, with a seventh (the Glasgow & South Western) approaching within nine miles at Gretna Junction.[6] Carlisle thus stood at the extremity of systems whose lines stretched as far as Oban and Aberdeen, Swansea and Southend. The significance of Carlisle as a junction lies in the interchange of traffic between the lines converging upon it from England and Scotland respectively. It is perhaps the greatest 'parting of the ways' in Britain. But in both road and railway the 'scale' by which its nodality is measured is national rather than local.

Newcastle shares something of this function as a node in the trunk road system, but to a much smaller degree. Of the five Ministry of Transport trunk roads converging on it, two are represented by the Great North Road (A.1) to Edinburgh and London respectively. The third (A.696–A.68) leads through the Southern Uplands at Carter Bar and is actually the shortest road to Edinburgh. The fourth is the Carlisle road (A.69) and the fifth (A.184) terminates at Sunderland little more than twelve miles away. But to these trunk roads are to be added a dozen first-class (A) roads which spread out in a dense mesh through the coalfield.

As a rail centre, too, the function of Newcastle is that of an exchange point between the main line and the Tyneside Conurbation. There is no forking of the main line either in a northerly or southerly direction, which, as we have seen, is what has made the nodality of Carlisle. There are, in fact, more railways converging on Newcastle than on Carlisle, but the great majority are lines carrying only local services. In other words on a local scale within the coalfield its nodality is greater than that of Carlisle; on a national scale it is less.

One thing, however, which Newcastle and Carlisle certainly have in common is an extreme concentration of communications on a single unmistakable centre represented by the cities themselves. In neither region is there any comparable meeting-place of road and railway. This is not always the case. Sometimes separate *foci* for road and rail respectively have grown up within

[6] The six companies were the L. & N.W.R., the Midland, the N.E.R., the North British, the Caledonian, and the Maryport & Carlisle.

a locality at different points; sometimes several points of concentration share the function for an industrial area. The Potteries provide an example of the former, the Middle Trent of the latter.

The Potteries (Fig. 32) are situated in the upper part of the

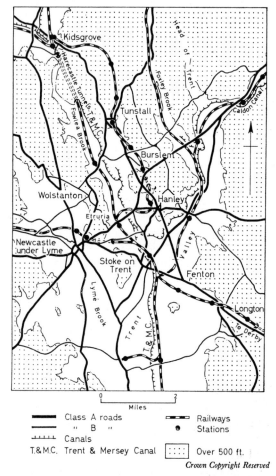

FIG. 32. THE COMMUNICATIONS OF THE POTTERIES

Trent basin, where a faulted pitching syncline brings the Coal Measures to the surface. Almost on the synclinal axis is the old market-town of Newcastle-under-Lyme. The Lyme Brook, which runs through it, is one of several right-bank tributaries of the Trent. Parallel with it to the north-east, and running from north-north-west to south-south-east, are the Fowlea and Foxley Brooks and the tiny stream which, to the south of Biddulph, bears the name of Trent. This stream swings south-west to cut off successively the Foxley, Fowlea, and Lyme Brooks. Between the Fowlea and Foxley Brooks is a cuesta which consists mainly of shales and marls, but contains also ironstones and coal seams. This cuesta lay within the ancient rural parishes of Wolstanton, Burslem, and Stoke-on-Trent which between them covered an area of nearly forty square miles. Within these parishes there grew up a number of centres of industrial activity based on the manufacture of pottery, and, although the industry goes back at least to the fourteenth century,[7] it was not until the eighteenth that the concentration of urban population on and around the cuesta began to overshadow the market-town of Newcastle-under-Lyme. Within this growing urban complex Stoke was not at first the largest unit. It had for long been of local importance as a bridging-point where the Newcastle–Derby road crossed the Trent, but at the Census of 1811 the township of Penkhull, in which it was included, had a population of only 3,851 as against 4,481 in Hanley, 5,487 in Shelton, 4,930 in Longton, and 8,625 in the whole parish of Burslem, most of whom lived in the township of that name. At the same time Newcastle-under-Lyme had a population of 6,175 and was still firmly established as the regional centre.

Since the present road-system is the product of the development and modernization of an element older than the Industrial Revolution, the rise of the newer urban centres, which collectively are far larger than Newcastle,[8] has not disrupted the old pattern. Newcastle is still a vital road centre on the main artery from the West Midlands to Merseyside and south Lancashire. The newer communications, however, virtually ignore the older town and have become centred on Stoke for two reasons. The first is that the 'pull' of the Potteries was already making itself felt when the Trent & Mersey Canal was completed in 1777, and still more so when the railway arrived in 1848. The second, perhaps more important, is that these newer kinds of communication, being more sensitive to the relief, were drawn together near the convergence of the Fowlea and Trent valleys. The main lines of both canal and railway use the valley of the Fowlea Brook and its continuation southwards in the Trent (or more strictly the parallel

[7] H. A. Moisley, 'The industrial and urban development of the North Staffordshire Conurbation'. *I.B.G., Trans. & Papers,* 17 (1951), p. 151.
[8] Populations (1951 Census): Newcastle-under-Lyme M.B. 70,036; Stoke-on-Trent C.B. 275,115.

abandoned valley just to the east of it), and each throws out a branch through the gap in the cuesta cut by the main river between Hanley and Fenton. In addition the railway has other branches, one via Fenton and Longton to the Blithe valley, another via Newcastle westwards into the Shropshire Plain and a third via Hanley to rejoin the Manchester line at Kidsgrove. This last winds its way up from Etruria on to the cuesta for the express purpose of serving the pottery towns of Hanley, Burslem, and Tunstall, which the line in the bottom of the Fowlea valley had been unable to reach. As a railway centre, therefore, Stoke has not only outstripped Newcastle, which is served by an intermediate station on a relatively unimportant branch line; it has also emerged as the nodal centre of the Potteries and has thereby endowed with its name a county borough which includes several towns at one time larger than itself.

If one follows the Trent downstream from the Potteries one eventually reaches an area of great importance in the communication system of the country. Its chief nodes are three in number, and they exhibit so well the different kinds of source from which a place can derive its nodality that it will be worth looking at them and their regional setting more closely. They are respectively Derby, Nottingham, and a section of the Trent valley near Long Eaton approximately half-way between the two (Figs. 33 and 34). The essential features of this piece of country may be summarized as follows:

(i) It lies at the southern extremity of a coalfield which stretches northwards for sixty miles.

(ii) It lies at a point where the Trent, having circumvented the southern end of the Pennines, is joined on the north side by a number of tributaries occupying well-defined valleys, while on the south side the River Soar, having passed round the eastern side of Charnwood Forest, provides a broader valley leading in the direction of Leicester and eventually of London.

(iii) In the sector between north and west there is a tract of upland of poor economic development beyond which, however, lie heavily populated urban areas. Straight lines drawn from London to Manchester and Leeds would pass respectively just to the west of Derby and just to the east of Nottingham.

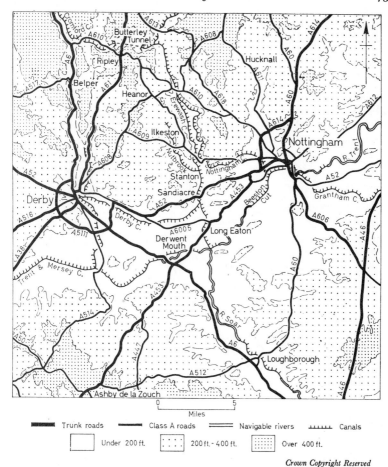

FIG. 33. THE ROADS AND CANALS OF THE DERBY–NOTTINGHAM
AREA

(iv) Lines of communication from north-east England to the
West Midlands and the south-west tend to be pushed
eastwards by the Southern Pennines and to pass through
the region.

(v) The head of navigation on the Trent is at Wilden Ferry, a
mile and a half above its confluence with the Derwent.

(vi) There is a considerable local population. On the coalfield
to the north this has resulted in the growth of a large
number of small towns like Belper, Ilkeston, Hucknall,
Heanor, Ripley, Alfreton, and the larger Mansfield, each

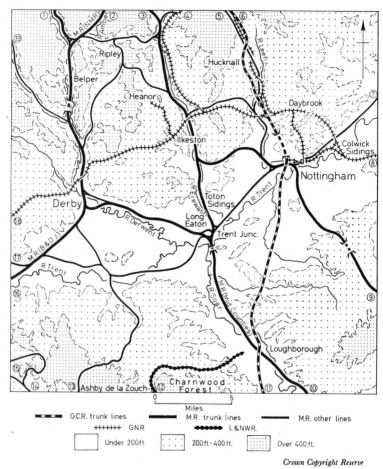

Crown Copyright Reserve

FIG. 34. THE RAILWAYS OF THE DERBY–NOTTINGHAM
AREA

Numbers in circles indicate routes to: 1, Manchester; 2 and 3, Chesterfield; 4, Shirebrook; 5, Mansfield; 6, Sheffield; 7, Newark and Lincoln; 8, Grantham; 9, London (St. Pancras) via Melton Mowbray; 10, London (St. Pancras) via Leicester; 11, London (Marylebone) via Rugby; 12, Coalville; 13, Ashby; 14, Moira; 15, Burton; 16, Birmingham; 17 and 18, Uttoxeter; 19, Wirksworth.

(except perhaps the last) too small to dominate the communication system yet large enough to be ranked as a local nodal centre. On the southern side towns of comparable size, such as Burton, Ashby-de-la-Zouch, Coalville,

Loughborough, and Melton Mowbray are more widely spaced, while behind them are scattered round the outfield, as it were, the larger centres of Wolverhampton, Birmingham, Coventry, and Leicester.

(vii) The Trent itself is wide enough to act as an effective barrier and is bridged only at infrequent intervals.

It is a combination of these circumstances in varying degrees which imparts the distinctive characteristics to the three nodes.

Derby lies on the River Derwent at a point where it emerges from the shallow valley by which it traverses the low foothills of the Pennines into the funnel-shaped flood-plain it has made for itself as it approaches the Trent. It is therefore particularly affected by its situation in relation to the population centres beyond the Derbyshire Dome (iii above). It has become a major road centre with no less than seven trunk roads converging on it, viz. Leicester (A.6), Nottingham (A.52), Chesterfield (A.61), Buxton–Manchester (A.6), Macclesfield (A.52–523), the Potteries (A.516–50), and Birmingham (A.38). No other town in Britain, below the rank of a major regional city like Manchester and Birmingham, has so many trunk roads separately entering its boundaries. As a railway centre, too, it has derived its importance from similar premises, but in this context it has been particularly susceptible to the influences of physical geography and has also enjoyed certain historical advantages. It was marked out early to be a major railway junction as a result of the railway developments of the Parliamentary Session of 1836. Among the numerous railways authorized in this Session were three whose lines terminated in Derby. To the south-east the Midland Counties Railway made for the Soar Valley and ran via Loughborough and Leicester to Rugby where it joined the London and Birmingham line already under construction. To the south-west the Birmingham & Derby Junction followed the Trent & Tame valleys to Birmingham and made another connexion with the London–Birmingham line at Hampton-in-Arden. The third company, the North Midland Railway, extended the system northwards by way of the Derwent and Amber valleys and thence into the Rother–Don drainage system. When, in 1844, these three companies amalgamated to form the Midland Railway, Derby found itself at the very centre of a system reminiscent of the three-legged symbol of the Isle of Man. Furthermore, within the next thirty years or so each of these 'legs' became greatly elongated, reaching respectively to London (St. Pancras), Bristol, and Carlisle. Historical processes therefore confirmed and accentuated the nodality of Derby within the Midland system, and this applied even more when the Manchester line was completed in 1867. Until this date the only practicable routes from London to Manchester were from Euston via Rugby and Crewe or Stoke (North Staffordshire Railway) or from King's Cross via Retford and Sheffield. The valley of the Derwent and its tributary the Wye bisected the large tract of country lying between the two routes, and by a process of extension in stages the Midland system used this physiographic opportunity to complete a line from London to Manchester fractionally longer than that via Crewe (mainly owing to less directness in the London–Derby section) but well able to compete for Manchester traffic. Other lines of more local significance were added to Ripley, Wirksworth, Uttoxeter, and the South Derbyshire Coalfield and in the eighteen-seventies the Great Northern Railway built a separate line through the town. But already Derby was established as the hub of the Midland Railway to an extent which was paralleled by no other town on any other system, and it was only logical that the company's administrative offices, as well as its locomotive, carriage, and wagon works, should be located there.

The city of Nottingham has much in common with Derby. They were both numbered among the Five Boroughs of Danish Mercia; they both emerged as county towns and they shared the general regional situation briefly outlined above. Nottingham (1951 population: 306,055) is much larger than Derby (141,267), but it has never achieved quite the same importance as a route-centre on a national scale. As we have seen, the roads converging on the Middle Trent valley from the west are naturally drawn into Derby, while on the eastern side there are few centres of comparable importance. The largest town on this side is Lincoln, and its connexions to the south-west are based on the Roman Fosse Way which was there long before Nottingham. There are in fact only four trunk roads converging on the city, viz: to Derby (A.52), Birmingham (A.453), Stamford (A.606., which, however, is a trunk road only as far as its junction with the Fosse Way at Widmerpool cross roads), and Bawtry (A.614). But as well as these there are some eight other first-class roads converging on the city, mainly from the coalfield sector. Its local accessibility area as shown on the O.S. map is at least as large as that of Derby and more heavily populated.

As a railway centre, too, Nottingham's nodality is not comparable with that of Derby on a national scale. It lacked the advantage of early establishment which Derby enjoyed, and at the time of consolidation of the Midland Railway (1844) it was still the terminus of a branch line from Trent, which, however, was soon extended to Lincoln. It was not placed on an important main line until 1880 when the route via Melton Mowbray and Corby was completed. This permitted the running of expresses from St. Pancras to Sheffield and the North (but not to Manchester) via Nottingham, and some services (e.g. 'The Waverley' between St. Pancras and Edinburgh) are still routed this way. The second main line to pass through Nottingham was not completed until 1898–9. This was the Great Central main line built to link up a network of railways in the North with London (Marylebone). Through traffic was of paramount importance and, owing to the already adequate provision of railways and to the financial strain involved in completing its main line, the company never succeeded in developing more than a rudimentary system of branch lines south of Annesley. The railway therefore passes through Rugby, Leicester, Loughborough, and Nottingham without any branches at all apart from short spur connexions with other companies' lines.

To the other company serving the city, the Great Northern, Nottingham remained virtually the terminus of a branch from the main line at Grantham. The quite elaborate system which grew up to the north and west was always primarily concerned with coal traffic, and, the objective being London, this passed on to the main part of the system by going round rather than through Nottingham. The element of nodality in the former Great Northern system is therefore represented by the large marshalling yards at Colwick situated to the east of the town where the line from the coalfield joins the Grantham–Nottingham branch. Trains from the coalfield and from Derby and Stafford could reach the Great Northern station in Nottingham by means of the Daybrook direct line, but it is significant that this is of single track compared with the double-track line to Colwick.

In some ways the most interesting of the three nodes is that which has grown up round (rather than in) Long Eaton. This is not an important road junction. The relief of the land in this area is rarely strong enough to prevent the free development of a road-system, and consequently the roads have been drawn into Derby and Nottingham. But with the canals and railways this is not so. They have both been strongly influenced by the valley-lines, and, in the case of the canals, by the rivers themselves. It is here that the Trent is joined by its principal right-bank tributary the Soar. Being navigable (with the aid of some artificial cuts) as far as Leicester, this river gives access to the Grand Union Canal and hence to the East Midlands and London. The mouth of the Soar is almost immediately opposite the valley of the small Erewash, a stream which, though not navigable itself, has provided a route-way for further canal development of a more limited kind. The Erewash Canal penetrated the heart of the coalfield and formed also the starting-point of the Cromford Canal which served an historically (rather than economically) important centre of the textile industry. It also provided the means of access to the Derby Canal at Sandiacre and the Nutbrook Canal at Stanton. A little lower down the Trent the Beeston Cut linked the main river with the Nottingham Canal, while further upstream Brindley fixed the terminus of his Trent & Mersey Canal, at the point where the flow of the Trent is considerably increased by the addition of the water of the Derwent, the Trent itself being navigable for only a mile and a half above this point. Here, then, was a major focal point in the water communications of England, which were far too intimately related to the river-systems to be drawn westwards to Derby or eastwards to Nottingham.

The arrival of the railways superimposed a similar figure on the Long Eaton area. The five railways which fan out from Trent Junction follow the five rivers: the Trent upstream, the Trent downstream, the Soar, the Derwent, and the Erewash. The junction was at first merely the point of bifurcation of the Notting-ham branch from the Rugby–Derby line. But from the outset there was a faction among the promoters of the Midland Counties Railway[9] in favour of taking it on to reach the collieries of the Erewash valley. Also the advent of the canal had encouraged the rise of other local industries, particularly ironworks, such as the Stanton Ironworks, and these made the valley a desirable objective in itself. The Erewash valley line was opened as far as Codnor Park in 1847 and in 1862 was extended to Clay Cross. It became a major collecting channel for coal traffic, and the location of the

[9] F. S. Williams, *The Midland Railway* (1877), pp. 23–25.

large marshalling yards at Toton is a direct reflection of this.[10]
But more, it provided an alternative and shorter route to the
north than that via Derby, and therefore Trent became the point
of separation for most of the Sheffield, Leeds, and Scottish traffic
from that destined for Derby and the Manchester line. That such
an important node in the Midland system was able to maintain
itself within ten miles of Derby bears witness to the influence
asserted by local economic, but more particularly, physical
geography on the growth of the railway system (Plate 33).

The situation of towns, or, as in this case, areas of high nodal
value, at the confluence of rivers is a common feature of settlement
geography, whether the rivers are navigable or not. Salisbury,
Northampton, and Peebles would serve as examples. Some large
industrialized towns, such as Sheffield and Huddersfield, possess
the same property. In Manchester the situation is more complicated. It is true that the city lies at the confluence of three
rivers, the Irwell, Irk, and Medlock, but the valleys of the two
last are too deep and winding to be of much use for communications. On the other hand the valleys of the Tame, Etherow, and
Goyt, all of which carry main lines of communication, converge
upon an area further to the south-east, and if physiography were
of paramount importance, Stockport would have a greater degree
of nodality than Manchester. The 'pull' of the big city, however,
has proved stronger, and the present main lines of railway leave
these valleys as they approach Stockport and make more directly
for Manchester.

If the word 'junction' is more familiar than 'node' it does
nevertheless need some qualification, as it lends itself to three
different interpretations. In the strictest, least familiar, and for
our purpose least important sense, it means simply the joining
together of lines belonging to different companies. This does not
necessarily imply any bifurcation or multiplication of routes. The
track belonging to one company may form a linear extension of
that belonging to another. The point of union is then known as
an 'end-on junction'. An example occurred, for instance, at Hawes
(Yorkshire), where the station at the head of the North-Eastern
Railway's Wensleydale branch was entered on the west by a
branch of the Midland. At Little Bytham in south Lincolnshire

---

[10] The lines at Trent Junction are all raised above the Trent flood-plain on embankments, and Toton is the nearest point up the Erewash valley where sidings could be
conveniently laid out.

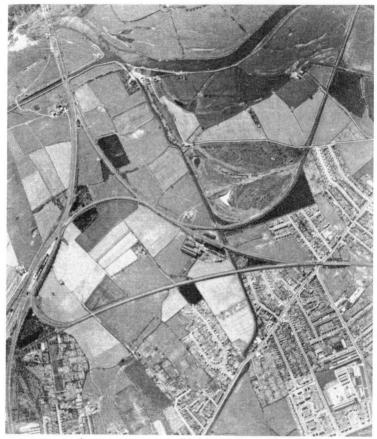

PLATE 33. TRENT JUNCTION, DERBYSHIRE

Emerging from the tunnel (top left), the main line of the former Midland
Railway immediately crosses the Trent and bifurcates. The original main line
to Derby leaves on the right on the photograph. The Nottingham branch
enters Trent Junction Station (left). The line in the corner (bottom, left) is
the Erewash valley main line. Further to the left still are the lines to Nottingham and (extreme left) Toton Sidings. The line which recrosses the Trent
(top, right) follows the main valley upstream to connect with the Birmingham
line south-west of Derby. An artificial cut can be seen leaving an unnavigable
section of the Trent (note the weir, top left). Near the same point the Grand
Union (Erewash) Canal enters the river at Trent Lock. The mouth of the Soar
can be seen just to the right of the railway bridge (top, left). Note the pattern
of residential access roads leading into the main road (A.453, Nottingham–
Birmingham). South at the top.

the Midland branch ended and the Midland & Great Northern line began. Shepreth Junction, near Cambridge, was simply a point where a change of ownership occurred between the former Great Northern and Great Eastern companies. To all appearances these stations look like ordinary intermediate stations on one continuous line. Only the initiated, versed in the different building styles and other practices of the old companies, could recognize them as junctions at all.

More usually junctions are formed by two or more lines converging to form one line by means of points. Since it is the union of the tracks which is important we may call these *'track-junctions'* or *'line-junctions'*.

The convergence of tracks leads to the convergence, and therefore the interchange, of traffic, and this may also be said to take place at a junction. Witney, Wolvercote, and Kennington Junctions are all track-junctions in the outskirts of Oxford, but the marshalling of trains and the changing of passengers takes place in Oxford itself which is therefore a junction of a different kind, to which the term *'traffic-junction'* is appropriate.

Very often the traffic-junction is located at, or very close to, the track-junction. Clapham Junction is perhaps the best-known example. Llandudno Junction, Doncaster, Ashford, and literally hundreds more would serve as other examples. Sometimes the point of divergence (the track-junction) is reached before the station (the traffic-junction) as at Carnforth (Lancashire) or Sutton (Surrey), and then the station lies between the diverging tracks (Plate 34).

On the other hand the track-junction may be quite remote from the traffic-junction to which it is related. The track-junction where the Liverpool line leaves the Euston–Glasgow main line is known as Weaver Junction, but any interchange of traffic between the two lines would take place at Crewe, some sixteen miles to the south-east. Crewe is the site of the track-junctions for several other lines (Fig. 20B) and has therefore become the principal traffic-junction too, and Weaver Junction is near enough to be operated from a traffic point of view as though the separation actually took place in Crewe.

How far a track-junction must be removed from a traffic-junction before it can no longer be effectively operated from it is a question to which there is no simple answer. It is a matter of working convenience deriving from the whole situation of the

Photo: Aerofilms, by permission of G. & G. Kynoch Ltd., Isla Bank Mills

PLATE 34. KEITH JUNCTION, BANFFSHIRE

The former Great North of Scotland Railway from Aberdeen (right) to Craigellachie and Elgin is seen curving towards the foreground. The point of separation between it and the most direct (Highland Railway) line to Elgin (left) occurs east of the station which lies between the diverging tracks. View to the north-east.

junctions and the nature of the traffic. Interchange of much traffic between the West Coast main line and the Furness district takes place at Carnforth, which is therefore a traffic-junction as well as a track-junction, yet it is situated only some six miles north of the traffic-junction of Lancaster. Many semi-fast trains stop and carry out separate interchange functions at both. On the other hand the track-junction at Kinnaber (Angus) is operated for traffic purposes as though it were a part of Aberdeen, twenty-eight miles away. A train from Aberdeen to Forfar and Perth is not in any way affected by the fact that the Dundee line makes a junction at this point, at any rate not as far as the interchange of traffic is concerned, and no provision for connexions is made in the time-table. Sometimes, again, the process of interchange for a track-junction may be shared by more than one traffic-junction. The Ipswich–Bury St. Edmunds and Ipswich–Norwich lines diverge at Haughley, and several passenger trains make connexions here for traffic between the Bury and Norwich lines, whereas others omit the Haughley stop but make a connexion in the next station in the Ipswich direction (Stowmarket). The interchange function is therefore shared between the two stations and changes in operational practice could at any time eliminate the one and concentrate the interchange wholly in the other, but the *track-junction* would remain at Haughley.

When one comes to consider the location of junctions this distinction between track-junctions and traffic-junctions if of paramount importance. Traffic-junctions again fall into two main groups as far as their location is concerned. In the one group are junctions situated in pre-existing urban areas into which several lines have been attracted. Nearly all large towns and many small ones are junctions of this kind. Birmingham, Newcastle, Carlisle, Peterborough, Salisbury, and so on were all towns before they were railway junctions. They formed obvious centres for the concentration, and therefore the junction, of railways. In the second group are those traffic-junctions which owe their origin to the nature of the railway network itself. Crewe, Swindon, Eastleigh, Hellifield, Carstairs, Bletchley, Normanton, and Melton Constable are examples. In each place there was no settlement larger than a village at the advent of the railway.

Many smaller junctions could be cited which, even after they were established, failed to attract settlement. Bowen writes of

the very large number of railway junctions in Wales, that, in spite of being communication centres, have no settlement whatever in their vicinity. Such are Dyfi Junction, on the borders of Cardiganshire, Montgomeryshire and Merionethshire, Moat Lane Junction in Montgomeryshire, Builth Road, Three Cocks and Talyllyn Junctions in Brecknockshire and Afon Wen Junction in Caernarvonshire.[11]

It was the selection of these sites as track-junctions which led to their development as traffic-junctions with or without associated settlement. In short where the location of traffic-junctions is not governed by the pre-railway urban settlement-pattern it is governed by the location of track-junctions, and our investigation can therefore be directed primarily towards these.

Several factors come into the location of track-junctions. To begin with there is a purely geometrical issue, which can be

[11] E. G. Bowen, *Wales: a Physical, Historical and Regional Geography* (1957), p. 226.

seen in its simplest form where a line passes near to a town and throws out a branch to it. The shortest line which can achieve this is one which approaches the main line at the nearest point, and

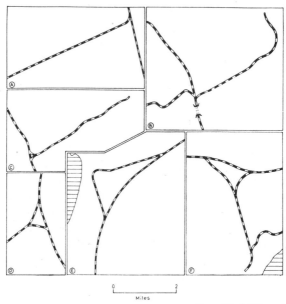

FIG. 35. RAILWAY JUNCTIONS

A. Cheddington (Bucks). Junction of the Aylesbury branch (left) with the former L.N.W.R. main line.
B. Kemble (Glos). Tetbury (left) and Cirencester (right) branches joining the former G.W.R. line from Paddington to Gloucester and Cheltenham.
C. Wolverton (Bucks). Newport Pagnell branch (right) joining the former L.N.W.R. main line.
D. Kilwinning (Ayrshire). Saltcoats and Ardrossan line (left) joining the main Glasgow–Ayr line of the former G. & S.W.R.
E. Weston-super-Mare (Som). Loop-line leaving and rejoining the Bristol–Exeter main line, former G.W.R.
F. Polegate (Sussex). Junction for the Eastbourne branch, former L.B. & S.C.R.

numerous track-junctions are situated in such positions. Cheddington (Fig. 35A) is a good example. The London & Birmingham Railway passed some seven miles to the east of Aylesbury and threw out a branch from the nearest point. Twyford (for Henley-on-Thames) and Tiverton Junction are similarly situated. Ramsey (Huntingdonshire) is approached by two terminal lines which connect with passing lines at Holme and Somersham respectively. At Kemble (Gloucestershire) terminal branches diverge at right angles on either side to Tetbury and Cirencester (Fig. 35B). Generally track-junctions of this kind are in relatively isolated situations since it is unlikely that a pre-existing town will happen to lie at a point which is geometrically determined in relation to a branch. In Strathmore, for instance, Alyth Junction and Kirriemuir Junction are at about the nearest points on the main line as it passes Alyth and Kirriemuir respectively. On the other hand the nearest point to Blairgowrie happened to be at the town of Coupar Angus which acts as the junction for the Blairgowrie branch.

All these junctions are of a simple type, and make connexions with the main lines by points facing in one direction only. Where running in either direction is or has been regularly undertaken a curve may be inserted to permit this. A triangular junction results as at Wolverton (Newport Pagnell branch). The points of entry into the main line are here close together (Fig. 35C). At Hest Bank (Morecambe L.N.W.R. branch) they are rather wider. The Largs branch joins the former G. & S.W. line near Kilwinning by track-junctions about a mile apart (Fig. 35D). The junctions for the Eastbourne branch (Polegate and Stone Cross) are even more widely separated (Fig. 35F).

By an extension of this process of separating the points of entry into the main line, it becomes possible to take a train out of the main line at one point, run it through the town and back on to the main line, thereby creating a loop line. This happens for instance at Weston-super-Mare (Fig. 35E), or, on a larger scale, at Sutton and Mablethorpe (Lincolnshire). Two good examples occur on the former C.L.C. line between Liverpool and Manchester where loops of this kind are thrown out to serve Widnes and Warrington respectively, giving rise to four track-junctions on the main line.

Sometimes converging lines do not establish contact immediately but run parallel for some distance before joining together. These 'delayed junctions' may be due to the need to save the provision of a special signal box to control the junction, or they may be due to differences in levels, which must obviously be equalized before the junction can take place. Examples of this occur at Laister Dyke (Bradford) and Hillmorton (Rugby). Often they will be found to occur where the converging lines belonged to different companies, as at Hitchin (Hertfordshire), where the former Great Northern and Midland lines run parallel for some distance before making contact. The same two companies owned the lines which take up a position side by side at Helpston in the Soke of Peterborough and from there run parallel with no physical connexions until they reach Peterborough some six miles away. By contrast the track-junction between the main line and the Boston line (both former Great Northern) just north of Peterborough, is encountered immediately at the point where the two lines approach each other (Werrington Junction).

The form and layout of a railway junction may also owe much to operational requirements. This is well exemplified in '*fly-over*' and '*burrowing*' junctions, in which the up and down tracks of the branch line are separated, one of them being carried over or under the main line. In this way interference with main-line traffic is avoided. Fly-over junctions can be seen at Weaver Junction (Cheshire), Worting (Hampshire) and Aynho (Buckinghamshire). A complicated example occurs at Black Carr Junction, Doncaster. Similar arrangements may be made in order to sort out different categories of traffic as they approach stations, without there necessarily being a convergence of routes at the point concerned. This happens, for instance, in the approaches to Euston, Liverpool Street, and London Bridge Stations.

A type of junction closely related in appearance to the fly-over or burrowing junction is to be found where some feature of the environment makes it more convenient for a line to diverge apparently in the wrong direction, that is to say to the right when its destination lies on the left of the line from which it is separated, and vice versa. The main line is then crossed by over-bridge or under-bridge shortly after. This happens, for instance, at Trowse Lower Junction outside Norwich Thorpe, and at Prospect Hill Junction, Whitby. Frequently, as in these two examples, considerable differences in levels are involved, with associated gradients which can be better accommodated in this way. Perhaps the best example is at Severn Tunnel Junction (Monmouthshire), where trains travelling eastwards to the tunnel fork to the *left* of the Gloucester line (that is to say away from the estuary) and pass underneath it again at a much lower level when they are in the tunnel. This is not strictly a 'burrowing' junction, since both tracks diverge on the same side and the fouling of the up Gloucester track by the down tunnel track is not avoided.

Although the general situation of most junctions is a geometrical concern, their *precise* situation is often strongly influenced by physical features. In particular three main kinds of physiographic situation have given rise time and again to the location of junctions. These are (i) convergent valley-routes, (ii) water-partings, and (iii) various other types of physical barrier.

Convergent valley-routes assert the most obvious kind of strong physiographic control over the situation of junctions. Syston (Leicestershire), Methley (Yorkshire), Bala Junction (Merioneth), and Ballinluig (Perthshire) are situated at the confluence of rivers whose valleys carry 'confluent' railways. Frequently, the nodality of such a situation will already have given rise to a town site in the pre-railway era, as has already been pointed out (p. 179). Sometimes the emergence of well-defined valleys in coastal lowlands gives rise to a junction as at Foryd (near Rhyl), where the Denbigh–Rhyl branch, following the broad *graben* of the Vale of Clwyd, meets the main line of the North Wales coast. A few miles further east, at Holywell Junction, a totally different type of valley, short, steep and ravine-like, brought in the little Holywell branch (Plate 4). The emergence of railways from narrow valleys into broad inland vales is in many ways comparable. The Chiltern-foot junction of Princes' Risborough is an example. Standish (Gloucestershire) is similarly situated where the Stroud valley emerges into the tract of lowland at the foot of the Cotswold scarp. Other good examples occur at Honeybourne (Gloucestershire) and Redhill (Surrey).

In junctions of this kind the railways are simply following very closely the configuration of the surface. The junctions themselves need not be situated in the valley-bottom. Stanley Junction (Perthshire), for instance, is related to the crossing of the Strathmore depression by the valley of the Tay. Its position is very strongly governed by the relief and drainage; but it lies on a higher bench outside the steep-sided valley in which the river flows.

Many junctions are situated on water-partings. In the rather rare cases where railways follow watersheds they may throw out branches down the various valleys as they pass their heads. This happens, for instance, on the Wakefield–Bradford line (p. 59), where laterals are or were thrown out at Lofthouse, Ardsley, Tingley, Drighlington, and Dudley Hill, all of which are junctions perched on the Aire-Calder watershed. Meldon and Halwill

(Devon) are similarly situated. Much more usual are those junctions which occur where a line, having climbed up to a watershed, is in a suitable position to gain access to more than one valley on the opposite side.

Very little of the county of Norfolk rises above the 300-foot contour and none of it reaches 350 feet. It seems somewhat absurd therefore that the M. & G.N. Railway selected one such eminence as the focal centre of its system. At Pigg's Grave the line reached a level of 312 feet, and just east of the summit four lines, from South Lynn, Norwich, Yarmouth, and Cromer, converged on the junction of Melton Constable, climbing, like the Duke of York's men, to the top of the hill, only to descend on the other side. An important traffic-junction, with locomotive sheds, a railway works, and a small but incongruously urban-looking settlement grew up on this unlikely spot. In fact Melton Constable lies on the fringe of four drainage-systems, those of the Wensum, Bure, Glaven, and Stiffkey, and these, particularly the first three, largely govern the routes of the approaching lines. What would seem at first sight to be unreasonable is really quite a straightforward adjustment to relief. Among other junctions situated on or near watersheds may be mentioned Hawes Junction (Garsdale —not to be confused with the 'end-on' junction in Hawes), Colbren (Breconshire), Parsley Hay (Derbyshire), if one can speak of a 'watershed' in limestone country, Mawcarse (Kinross), Gleneagles (Perthshire), and Georgemas (Caithness). Blakey Junction, on the abandoned Rosedale Mineral Branch (North Yorkshire), stood on the Farndale-Rosedale watershed at over 1,200 feet.

Physical barriers often determine the location of junctions. In a sense watersheds are merely one form of barrier, but in the present group one has in mind physical obstacles such as rivers or hills which can be crossed only by expensive structures such as bridges, tunnels, or deep cuttings. Duplication would be an unnecessary expense and lines tend therefore to be drawn together so as to make use of the one structure. The Great Central & Hull & Barnsley Joint line from the South Yorkshire Coalfield ran northwards to enter the Hull & Barnsley main line at a point known as Aire Junction near Gowdall, immediately at the head of the bridge over the River Aire. This was the most easterly point at which it could possibly make the junction without having to cross the river by a separate bridge. Other junctions of this type are found at Ford (Sussex) where the Arun is crossed, at Sutton

Bridge (Lincolnshire) on the Nene, and at Barmouth Junction (Merioneth), now known as Morfa Mawddach. At Gainsborough (Lincolnshire) the railways have been drawn together into the town, but the plan (Fig. 36) makes it clear that the crossing of the Trent has been the main factor determining the layout of lines.

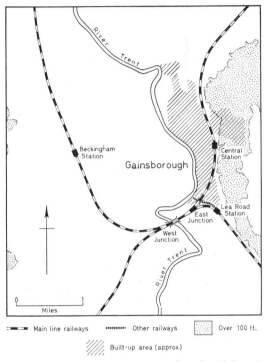

Crown Copyright Reserved

FIG. 36. RAILWAYS AT GAINSBOROUGH, LINCS

Sometimes tunnels, rather than bridges, provide the bottleneck which draws lines together. Among the longer tunnels which have junctions situated immediately at the tunnel-end are Harecastle (Staffordshire) and Bradway (Yorkshire). A particularly good example occurs at Hilton, where the lines approaching Perth from the south have to tunnel through a steep little cuesta to reach the city centre. The junction is situated immediately outside the south portal.

Although road and canal junctions must be examined in the light of their own particular requirements, the same principles will help to elucidate their location. The canal junctions shown in Figure 16, for instance, are the unmistakable equivalents of 'watershed' railway junctions. All occur within three miles at most of the Avon water-parting. In the same way road junctions may be found in situations which reflect the 'geometrical' setting rather than the urban pull, though the more elaborate installations of railway junctions may be matched only by the traffic roundabout, the filling-station, and the transport café. In a few cases—Scotch Corner is an excellent example of a road junction which owes everything to its situation—there may be an hotel. Sometimes there are no strong physical features involved. Mere Corner (Cheshire) and Cadnam (Hampshire) are only weakly controlled by physiography. Perhaps the main difference between the roads and the railways in this respect lies in the fact that ancient roads, on which many of our present roads are based, grew up hand-in-hand with the urban settlement-pattern. Isolated road junctions are therefore relatively less common. The advent of the 'Motorway' may alter this.

The systematic study of the location of junctions, particularly in the approach to towns, is one which has so far received practically no attention in any published work. For anyone interested in applying the questions 'Where?' and 'Why there?' to this particular subject, there is a fascinating opportunity.

CHAPTER VIII

AIRWAYS AND OTHER FORMS OF TRANSPORT

Although roads, railways, and canals have some properties peculiarly their own, it has been possible so far to make certain assumptions which are valid for all of them. However widely they may differ in their relationship to the land-surface, they have at least this in common, that they appear as continuous linear features of land use connecting geographically separated places. The construction and situation of these units must take into account the whole nature of the land-surface between all their points of origin and destination. One can therefore speak of gradients, curves, junctions, etc., knowing that one is referring to concepts which are applicable, though in different ways, to all of them. The geography of air transport, however, is based upon quite different premises and in any discussion of it the use of such terms in anything like the same sense would be meaningless. In attempting to follow the 'anatomical' approach one finds oneself looking for lines of communication which simply do not exist as tangible objects. Secondly, whereas we have so far regarded the external communications of Britain as lying outside our field of investigation and have had little difficulty in distinguishing between what is external and what is internal, airways pose a somewhat different problem. There are no airports in Britain dealing exclusively with internal traffic, however we may define it, and of those services which are generally regarded as internal a high proportion deal with areas separated by sea from the British mainland. It follows, therefore, that to make a fruitful study of the geography of air transport would involve an emphasis on traffic rather than on physical installations and an expansion of the subject into a much wider geographical field. Fortunately a recent study of this kind is available[1] and the reader is referred to it as an informative and very readable work. No attempt will here be made to do more than set the air communications of this country

[1] K. R. Sealy, *The Geography of Air Transport* (1957).

into their geographical perspective and to look briefly at some of the points of comparison which they invite with other forms of transport. While dealing with communications which are 'different' it will be convenient also to look briefly at some other and perhaps less familiar forms of transport which in various ways do not conform to the generalizations so far made.

The total volume of internal air traffic in Britain is still small in comparison with that of road or rail, because the particular circumstances applying in Britain do not give full play to its advantages. Of these saving of time is undoubtedly the chief, though comfort may also be a consideration. Saving of time, however, must be related to the whole of a journey, and higher speeds in the air may be more than offset by time wasted before and after the flight. Generally speaking, therefore, the advantage in favour of aviation tends to be most marked where the time-discrepancy is greatest, that is on long journeys or on shorter journeys where the alternative available forms of transport have to suffer even greater interruptions or hindrances, as happens particularly where sea-crossings are involved. This means that the demand for air services is very unevenly distributed. It is related to the distribution of population, and the relative isolation of potential traffic centres, and it is on the basis of this uneven demand that one can explain the distribution of airports within broadly defined localities. The importance of the airports in the Channel Islands and the Isle of Man, for instance (Fig. 37), reflects a large influx of population especially in the holiday season. The same would hold good of Blackpool or Margate or any other large resort, but whereas holiday-makers can reach such destinations perhaps as quickly and certainly more cheaply by other means, the alternative confronting the traveller to these island resorts is a sea-crossing. The precise situation of airports, however, within those localities is the product of many other considerations which Sealy has set out in general terms as well as with particular reference to the airports of London.[2] Seven main factors emerge from this discussion.

First there are the technical properties of the aircraft. By determining length and strength of runway these primarily control the area of land required. Secondly, and arising directly out of the

[2] K. R. Sealy, 'London's Airports and the Geography of Airport Location'. *Geography*, xi (1955), p. 255.
See also R. J. Double, 'London Airport'. *Town Planning Rev.* xxix (1958), p. 79.

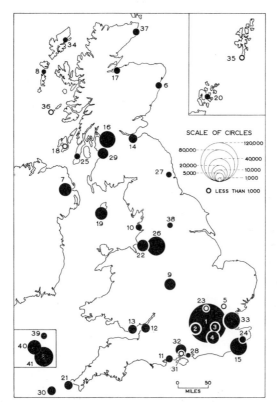

FIG. 37. AIR TRANSPORT MOVEMENTS AT AERODROMES IN THE
U.K. AND CHANNEL ISLANDS, 1958

The area of the circles is proportionate to the total number of landing and take-
off movements of all commercial flights (scheduled and charter) at aerodromes
which send regular returns to the Ministry of Transport and Civil Aviation.
(Figures under 1,000 are not shown proportionately.)

† indicates U.K. Customs Airport. 1, †London Airport. 2, †Blackbushe. 3, †Croy-
don. 4, †Gatwick (figures for last 7 months of 1958 only). 5, †Stansted. 6, Aberdeen
(Dyce). 7, †Belfast (Nutts Corner). 8, Benbecula. 9, †Birmingham (Elmdon). 10,
Blackpool (Squires Gate). 11, †Bournemouth (Hurn). 12, †Bristol (Lulsgate Bottom).
13, †Cardiff (Rhoose). 14, †Edinburgh (Turnhouse). 15, †Ferryfield. 16, †Glasgow
(Renfrew). 17, Inverness (Dalcross). 18, Islay (Port Ellen). 19, †Isle of Man (Ronaldsway). 20, Kirkwall. 21, Lands End (St. Just). 22, †Liverpool (Speke). 23, Luton.
24, †Lympne. 25, Macrihanish. 26, †Manchester (Ringway). 27, †Newcastle (Wool-
sington). 28, Portsmouth. 29, †Prestwick. 30, Scilly Isles (St. Mary's). 31, †South-
ampton Water. 32, †Southampton (Eastleigh). 33, †Southend (Rochford). 34,
Stornoway. 35, Sumburgh. 36, Tiree. 37, Wick. 38, †Yeadon. 39, Alderney. 40,
Guernsey. 41, Jersey.

Source: Summary of Activity at Aerodromes in the U.K. and the Channel Islands, 1958,
q.v. for methods of compilation, etc.

first, there are important physiographic requirements which have to be met.

Physically it must be an area of low relief, with clear unobstructed approaches permitting a descent angle of about 1 : 50, while the field itself must be as near flat as possible in order to minimise the cost of runway and drainage construction. The surface should be capable of bearing concentrated loads, and at the same time be free from flooding.[3]

Thirdly there are meteorological conditions, which in air communications still play a very important part. Fourthly there are the land-links with associated urban centres; fifthly the necessity for the provision of associated installations dealing with the maintenance and operation of aircraft and with the movement of passengers and the handling of freight. These will add to the demands of the airport on land use. The sixth consideration relates to the pattern of air routes converging on the airport and their relative importance, a situation on the side from which the dominant traffic approaches being desirable. Lastly the question arises whether the traffic of the district can be satisfactorily handled at a single airport or whether two or more airports need to be provided.

Sealy's discussion, of which the foregoing represents the barest précis, is a prelude to an examination of the location of London's airports and it would be pointless to repeat his work here in detail. However, it may be excusable to amplify some of the points by reference to other examples.

On physiographic grounds the choice of potential sites for an airport within easy reach of a large city is generally extremely limited. As might be expected certain types of landform tend to recur. Those landforms in which a level surface is well developed in two dimensions are particularly suitable, whether they have been formed by erosion or deposition, and in this respect the demand is somewhat different from that of roads, railways, and canals. Coastal landforms form the basis for many airports, for instance Islay (Plate 35), Tiree, and Ronaldsway (Isle of Man). The landforms themselves may be of various kinds. Liverpool (Speke) is built mainly on blown sand; Blackpool (Squires Gate) entirely so. Prestwick is virtually confined to a raised beach. Ferry-field (Lydd) spreads over the shingle, sand, and alluvium of Dungeness. But even in coastal situations upland landforms may

[3] Sealy, op. cit. (1955), p. 256.

Crown Copyright Reserved—Royal Air Force Photograph

PLATE 35. ISLAY AIRPORT

The airport occupies a site on the flat land fringing Laggan Bay. The straight line on the left is the A.846 road from Port Ellen (top) to Bowmore. The small Machrie River limits the extension of the airport on the Port Ellen side. The top of the photograph is to the south-east.

offer the sort of facilities which are needed. Cardiff (Rhoose) and Lympne, for instance, are both on coastal sites, yet both are separated from the sea by cliffs. Rhoose stands at a little over 200 feet at the top of the cliffs of the Lower Lias. Lympne stands at over 300 feet, again on the cliff-top, though here recent shoreline development has taken place below the old cliff-line and the sea has begun to recede. River-terraces afford some of the best sites. London Airport occupies one of the broadest stretches to be found anywhere in the Taplow Terrace.

Meteorological conditions are of paramount importance in aviation. Many of the problems they introduce, such as high-altitude and high-temperature take-off difficulties, are not encountered in Britain, but local climate has played an important part in airport location, particularly where visibility is affected by the incidence of fog. This in turn is the product of many factors. Relief and liability to rainfall, temperature inversions in low-lying land, and the occurrence of industrial smoke are among the more influential. Some areas of the country are more prone to fogs than others.[4] This does not prevent the building of airports if economic conditions warrant,[5] but local conditions are important. It is generally found, for instance, that the prevailing south-westerly winds make a situation to the south or west of a large city preferable to one on the north or east. This is confirmed by London Airport, Croydon, Manchester (Ringway), Glasgow (Renfrew), Edinburgh (Turnhouse), and Cardiff (Rhoose). Where other situations have been chosen there is generally an explanation. Birmingham Airport, for instance, is at Elmdon on the eastern side of the city. The southern and western environs are much more hilly and in places far more affected by industrial smoke (the Black Country). Of the London group of airports[6] only Stansted lies outside the south-western sector and this is situated some 33 miles from the centre. For some years after the war the discussion about the siting of an airport for north-east England was largely concerned with the question of the incidence of 'sea-frets' in the area between Newcastle and Sunderland.

The land communications between airports and the urban centres which they serve are of the greatest possible importance. It is here that the time is lost which places air transport at such a disadvantage on the shorter routes. Figure 38 makes this clear. From London to Aberdeen the fastest air schedule in August 1958 was less than half the fastest train schedule. To Edinburgh and Glasgow it was about half. To Manchester, Liverpool, and Newcastle the air service had a slight advantage only, and to Birmingham it was considerably quicker to go by train either from Euston

---

[4] Sealy, op. cit. (1957), pp. 46–47.

[5] With improved instruments this aspect of airport location is likely to prove relatively less important but up to the present it has asserted a powerful influence.

[6] London Airport, Gatwick, Blackbushe, Stansted, and (formerly) Croydon.

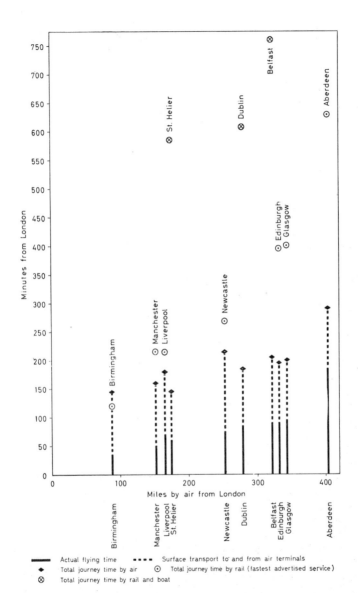

FIG. 38. COMPARATIVE TRAVELLING TIMES FROM LONDON BY AIR AND RAIL. SUMMER, 1958

Note: The times shown for surface transport to and from air terminals are the *minimum* times given in Bradshaw's Air Guide.

Sources: Bradshaw's Air Guide; Bradshaw's Railway Guide

or Paddington, although the actual flying time was booked as only 35 minutes. Efforts are at present being made to improve the surface transport facilities in London. The provision of the new West London Air Terminal and the road improvements between it and London Airport have eased the situation and will do so still more, but the surface transport times still stand at 60 minutes and over. The comparable times to Gatwick are much lower (40 minutes) although it is about twice as far out as London Airport, and this is due to the use of rail as against road transport. This, however, is quite exceptional, and nearly all British airports have to rely exclusively on road connexions. The provision of adequate rail contact could do much to reduce surface transport times, but the cost would be high and could only be contemplated where the expectation of traffic was good, particularly if existing railways pass near the airport. One of the main advantages of Gatwick is that the airport is immediately adjacent to the main London–Brighton line, and virtually all that was necessary to complete a really efficient rail link was the provision of a new station (Plate 36).

The provision of associated installations is a requirement which makes further demands on land use, and these tend to increase as the traffic of the airport increases. The report of the Millbourn Committee[7] emphasized the importance of this aspect. Its recommendations included the provision at London Airport of new terminal buildings for long-haul passenger flights, a freight building with floorspace of 300,000 square feet, an increase in parking space from 47 to 76 acres, and more land to be taken up by improved road approaches. It was suggested that the actual runway accommodation should be reduced by the closing of Runway 4, but even this would only partially solve the problem of insufficient space, and negotiations should be pressed forward for the acquisition of more land mainly for maintenance.

The direction of approach of the main air routes does not seem to have affected very markedly the location of British airports in relation to the land areas they serve. Pressure on land and the availability of sites suitable on other grounds are generally more important considerations. Neither can the question of multiplicity of airports be said to arise in connexion with any city except London. As a regional issue, however, this is much more real, and in recent controversies about the retention or abandoning of air-

[7] London Airport Development Committee (1957).

Photo: Aerofilms

PLATE 36. GATWICK AIRPORT

Gatwick has easily the best contact with land communications of any airport in Britain. The station was specially constructed on the main line from London to Brighton. View to the north-west.

ports, the situation of alternatives has been recognized as of major importance. It was argued, for instance, that Yeadon (Yorkshire) was too near to Ringway to warrant the cost of its maintenance as a working unit. Several airports similarly situated may be regarded as marginal, in the sense that the regions which they serve are not sufficiently productive of traffic to justify unequivocally the existence of more than one.

Some of the foregoing arguments, such as those relating to physiography and meteorology, are as relevant to military as to civil airfields, but the reasons governing their regional distribution are different. These are primarily related to strategic needs, and during the Second World War a tremendous development of airfields took place on the eastern side of Britain. Urban accessibility was not an important consideration, as many an ex-R.A.F. man will testify, and there was therefore generally a wider choice of site than for a civil airport, particularly since most of eastern Britain is comparatively level. East Anglia was particularly suitable for this purpose. On the Fakenham Sheet (O.S. one-inch Seventh Series No. 125) no less than sixteen airfields are marked, the great majority of them having reverted to agricultural use by now. Another favourite site was on the dipslopes of some of the cuestas of the East Midlands. The Lincolnshire Limestone escarpment, for instance, is crowned by a line of airfields stretching north and south from Lincoln. The situations of military airfields often preclude their conversion for civil use.

Among lesser-known forms of transport aerial ropeways call for some special mention. There seems to be no record of the total mileage of aerial ropeways at present operating in Britain, but under some conditions they have distinct advantages over other forms of transport. Provided the supporting trestles are high enough, aerial ropeways need not interfere with land use along the line of route except where the trestles themselves are standing. It has been computed[8] that 'ropeway trestles occupy only one eighty-fourth of the ground space per mile utilized by road or rail tracks'. The crossing of other lines of communication can be achieved without fouling them and uneven terrain can be crossed without difficulty. The maximum gradients which can be employed are much steeper than for other forms of transport, 1 in 2 being about the limit.

Although in other countries ropeways are used for passenger transport their contribution in Britain is almost entirely confined to the mining and quarrying industries. Here again their technical properties make them particularly well suited to this kind of work. For instance, it is possible by pre-selection to determine an exact point of automatic discharge, an invaluable asset in building up waste heaps. Other advantages are low running costs, low manpower requirements, and considerable durability.

Aerial ropeways are used extensively by the National Coal Board particularly in South Wales, where problems of waste disposal are complicated by the terrain and may involve severe gradients if waste has to be lifted out of the valleys. But they are by no means confined to this type of environment and are much employed at collieries in the East Midlands Division where the surface is relatively level. They are also used in the East Midlands ironstone field, for example near Desborough. Brick and tile manufacturers find them convenient for the transport of their raw

[8] W. Gilmore (British Ropeway Engineering Co. Ltd.), 'Aerial Ropeways'. *Mechanical Handling* (April 1954).

materials and in the brick-making country around Peterborough ropeways share the task with light railways. Between 1927 and 1932 some 2½ miles of ropeway were installed at Billingham (Co. Durham) to meet the internal transport problems of the I.C.I. works. Ropeways are in use in slate quarries in North Wales, limestone quarries, for instance at Cornelly, Glamorgan, and have particular advantages in gravel pits, where old workings, often liable to flood, aggravate the problems of surface forms of transport.

The word 'pipeline' generally calls to mind the great oil-producing countries of the world, and by comparison the use of pipelines in Britain for conveying petroleum, chemicals, etc. is very limited. Mention is made in Chapter IX of the oil pipeline across central Scotland, and others exist, for instance from Swansea Docks and more recently Milford Haven to the Llandarcy refinery (Glamorgan). In the chemical industry, too, many miles of pipeline have been laid, for instance on Teesside. But by far the most important use of pipelines is for the conveyance of water. The construction of long-distance aqueducts has become so much a commonplace that the mere statement that Birmingham derives its water from central Wales is no longer impressive. To some it may seem novel to include this under the heading of 'communications' at all. Yet in 1957–8 the provision of Birmingham with its water-supply involved the movement of over eighteen million ton-miles per day as far as the city boundary. Expressed in another way, this means that over a quarter of a million tons of water which would naturally flow down the Wye to Chepstow every day are instead conveyed across the Severn and eventually released in the Humber drainage-system. The feat is no less remarkable because it is accomplished entirely by gravitation.[9]

The gradient-profile of an aqueduct is very different from that of other forms of communication. The Elan Aqueduct (Fig. 39) will illustrate the principles involved. Where possible the aqueduct takes the form of conduits falling gently on regular gradients varying between 1 in 3,000 and 1 in 6,000, but mainly at 1 in 4,000. Since, however, the drainage of the intervening area is mainly across the line of the aqueduct, the maintenance of a uniform grade throughout is impossible. Where valleys have to be crossed, the conduits are replaced by pipes. These pipes (2 × 42 inches and 2 × 60 inches diameter) descend at much steeper gradients

[9] I am grateful to the General Manager and Secretary, City of Birmingham Water Department, for communicating much information on the City's water-supply.

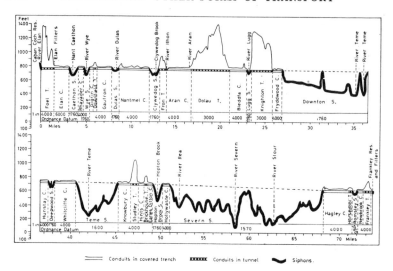

FIG. 39. THE ELAN AQUEDUCT

Section along the aqueduct from Caban Côch, near Rhayader (Radnorshire) to Frankley, Birmingham.

By courtesy of the General Manager and Secretary, Birmingham Water Department

and are able to rise again theoretically to the same height. In order to main an adequate flow, however, an 'hydraulic gradient' is employed in these 'siphons', as they are called, which is steeper than the grade of the conduits. Generally the gradient in the siphons is 1 in 1,760, but in the long Severn Siphon it is 1 in 1,570. Very high pressures are encountered in the siphons.

This combination of conduit and siphon means that for some sixty miles the aqueduct can be laid in covered trench with generally about three feet of cover, and there is therefore a close correlation between the aqueduct and the configuration of the ground. But at nine points tunnelling is necessary to carry the aqueduct between the several drainage-systems, and these tunnels collectively comprise some thirteen miles of route. Only at the crossings of streams and rivers are the pipes exposed. The behaviour of water in high-pressure pipes and gently graded conduits therefore governs the relationship to the land-surface[10] and results in a profile of a particular and wholly distinctive form.

A study of the profile and plan of other aqueducts would reveal broadly similar features (Plate 5). The Haweswater Aqueduct, for

[10] H. Addison, *A Treatise on Applied Hydraulics* (1954), p. 204 et seq.

instance, which supplies some 30 per cent. of Manchester Corporation's total requirements, is constructed on exactly the same principles. Through the Forest of Bowland and the Rossendale hills tunnels maintain conduits at gentle gradients comparable with those on the Elan line, while the valleys of the Lune, Ribble, and other rivers, which again run across the route of the aqueduct, are crossed by high-pressure siphons.[11]

In the Highlands of Scotland many miles of aqueduct have been constructed in connexion with hydro-electric development, so that the waters of the natural drainage basin of the Rannoch–Tummel, for instance, are supplemented by water collected in the Errochty, Garry, Bruar, and other smaller streams. Similarly in North Wales leets or open conduits on the eastern side of the Harlech Dome divert water from the Afon Eden system into that of the Prysor so as to swell the volume of water available for the Ivy Bridge (Maentwrog) Power Station.

The provision of special channels for the conveyance of water may take on a wide variety of forms. Two contrasting extremes may be found in Central London. On the one hand the sewers represent specially adapted conduits designed to lead away sewage to the outfalls at Beckton on the north of the Thames and Crossness on the south. On the other hand the London Hydraulic Power Company possesses a compact and intensive network of high-pressure pipes for the transmission of hydraulic power to numerous and highly diverse users.[12] The differences in the form and layout of these two systems reflect their totally different objectives and requirements.

Although it is clearly in the interests of economy that pipelines shall go by the most direct practicable route, and although, where the main function of the pipeline is to convey fluids in bulk between single points of origin and destination, this can often be achieved, the time-factor does not operate in demanding the same degree of directness as is necessary in other communications. Gas mains, for instance, where circumstances demand, may follow quite devious routes. The Chairman of the South-Western Gas Board has said: 'High pressure inter-connecting mains have been routed to supply the optimum number of consumers *en route*, and in some cases deviated slightly to afford supplies to isolated

[11] Information kindly supplied by the Engineer and Manager, Manchester Corporation Waterworks.

[12] *Administrative County of London Development Plan; Analysis* (1951), pp. 192–3.

villages.'[13] And again 'Bulk transmission mains are planned to pass through many such (isolated) communities, and there must be no hesitation in affording supplies in these cases direct from the high-pressure mains.'[14] The resulting pattern tends to be somewhat angular and indirect, totally unlike a modern road or a railway. As far as physiographic control is concerned considerable variations in altitude can be tolerated. The North Wales gas pipeline reaches an elevation of 1,750 feet above sea-level in Snowdonia, but in the South Wales Coalfield the concentration of both producer and consumer in the valleys has resulted in a distinctive figure of parallel lines, repeating the pattern of other communications and accentuating the lines of drainage.[15]

The pattern of lines associated with the transmission of electric current is again somewhat different. The electricity grid, unlike the gas grid, cannot be tapped except at stations specially equipped with expensive installations. Trunk and local distribution is more effectively separated than in any other form of transport, since quite distinct networks operating at different voltages are required for each purpose. The trunk (grid) lines therefore tend to proceed by the most direct route between power or sub-stations. Only in hilly country is the relief strong enough to affect the line of route appreciably, and transmission lines generally run across country irrespective of roads or other communications. But in the Grampian Highlands the lines serving the hydro-electric power stations do tend to run parallel with the roads since the mountains are high enough and rugged enough to confine both to the valleys, which is why, in travelling through the Highlands, one forms the impression that the whole country is studded with pylons. The road between Callander and Killin, for instance, and most of the road along Loch Tay, are paralleled by high-voltage transmission lines connecting Tummel Bridge with central Scotland.

The part played by ferries in the internal communications of Britain is still considerable in some areas. In addition to the more obvious situations in which ferries are used to connect islands or island groups with the mainland and with each other, ferries are employed to provide short-cuts where estuaries and arms of the sea would otherwise give rise to wide detours (Fig. 40). They are

[13] C. H. Chester, 'The organization of the gas industry in the South West'. *Institution of Gas Engineers, Publication No. 442* (1954), pp. 24–35.
    [14] ibid.
    [15] See also G. Manners, 'Recent changes in the British gas industry'. *I.B.G., Trans. & Papers,* 26 (1959), 153.

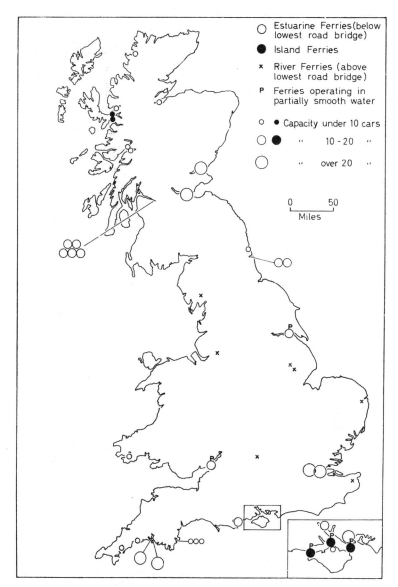

FIG. 40. FERRIES IN GREAT BRITAIN, 1948

Vehicular ferries in Great Britain operating within smooth or partially smooth water limits. The figures given for the capacity of the craft used are approximate.

Source: Ferries in Great Britain. Report of the committee appointed by the Ministry of Transport.
H.M.S.O., 1948

therefore common on those coasts where 'drowning' of valleys has been pronounced, for instance the fjord coast of western Scotland and the ria coasts of southern England. Frequently alternative routes are available, as at Ballachulish (Argyll), where the ferry saves about twelve miles between Glencoe and Fort William, though the route number (A.82) is given to the road which goes round by Kinlochleven. The gap in A.894 at Kylesku (Sutherland) is barely a quarter of a mile wide, but the journey which motor traffic would face in crossing from one side of the loch to the other if there were no ferry would be not much less than a hundred miles.

Although ferries of this kind may form essential links in the road-system of large tracts of country they do not generally carry very heavy traffic. By contrast the most important ferries tend to be found where urban development has taken place on or near the banks of rivers which are too wide to be bridged or are bridged further upstream. The Clyde below Glasgow and the Tyne below Newcastle are each crossed by several vehicular ferries. On the estuaries of the Tay and Humber the positions of Dundee and Hull have determined the present crossing points, though in both examples there were earlier ferry-points elsewhere. The principal ferry-points over the Forth at Queensferry (Plate 18) and the Severn at Aust are rather related to the narrowing of the estuaries at these places respectively. Similarly at Torpoint and Saltash the main roads from South Devon and Cornwall cross the ria of the Hamoaze at two of its narrowest places.

Ferries are to some extent an anomaly in the modern transport system. Even the best of them are slow, some are unreliable, depending on tidal conditions, some provide only an infrequent service and some are expensive. A few of those at present in operation, including some of those carrying the heaviest traffic, are likely to disappear as they become replaced by the bridges or tunnels referred to in the next chapter. But unquestionably there will be many where economic or physiographic conditions, or a combination of both, will make their replacement unjustifiable or impossible.

CHAPTER IX

POST-WAR PLANS AND PROGRESS

In a previous chapter we examined some of the ways in which communications can be recognized as the legacy of past periods. At any given date the most important formative period is not necessarily that of the immediate past. It is arguable that, from the point of view of geographical spread, the seventeen-nineties and the eighteen-forties had a greater influence on the growth of the canals and railways respectively than had any comparable period since. On the other hand the most recent phase of development always has a special significance because it reflects the impact of contemporary ideas, because generally people are better informed and more interested in matters which are in the news than those which are a part of earlier history, and because in the events of the recent past one finds the evidence on which to base the most reliable—or least unreliable—forecasts of the shape of things to come. This final chapter, therefore, will attempt a brief survey of some of the problems, plans and places which have figured in the newspapers in connexion with communications in the last ten or fifteen years. The background of economic and social change during this period has made it particularly important. Large parts of the transport system have passed into the control of the state, and this has created both the necessity and the opportunity for programmes of adjustment, many of which have brought and are bringing far-reaching geographical consequences.

As elements in the communication system of Britain the canals and navigable waterways are the subject of two opposite misconceptions. On the one hand they are regarded as back numbers, precluded by their very nature from playing an efficient part in twentieth-century transport. Speed limits of three to five miles per hour are quite usual, and much additional time may be spent in locks. On the other hand it is sometimes urged that only inefficiency in management and a deliberate desire for their extinction on the part of the railways have brought about the decline of canals, and that if they can meet modern needs cheaply and efficiently in other countries they should be able to do so here.

Two recent reports, the Rusholme[1] and Bowes[2] Reports, in addition to making specific recommendations, have done much to publicize the facts and bring the canals into their true economic perspective. The lists of canals recommended for retention and improvement in the two Reports do not quite agree, though the discrepancies are small (see Appendix C).

British Waterways did not wait for the publication of the Bowes Report before implementing the recommendations of the Rusholme Committee to the extent of preparing a £5½ million Development Plan for Group I Waterways. The geographical apportioning of this money, the location of the waterways concerned, and their 1955 tonnages are shown in Fig. 41. From this it can be seen that, without exception, the Group I Waterways, which were those found by the Rusholme Committee to be paying their way in the period 1951–3,[3] form navigable extensions of estuaries of great commercial importance. The Humber, Mersey, Severn, and Thames all contain important ports whose activities are closely associated with inland water transport. The nature of the traffic varies considerably with the specialization of the port and the economic geography of its hinterland. On the Aire & Calder Navigation, for instance, the influence of the Yorkshire Coalfield is pronounced. In 1953 coal accounted for almost 70 per cent. of the originating tonnage.[4] On the Sheffield and South Yorkshire Navigation the figure was over 96 per cent. On the Rivers Weaver and Severn coal formed a negligible proportion. The area served by the Weaver is dominated by the chemical industry while the Severn has proved a convenient artery for the movement of petroleum between Avonmouth and the West Midlands Conurbation. Some 82 per cent. of its originating tonnage in 1953 was returned as 'liquids'. It is not therefore the nature of the traffic which is the common element in these waterways but rather their situation in relation to the estuaries and the ports. The pattern in Figure 41 suggests a reversion towards the map of navigable waterways in the pre-canal era. And herein lies

---

[1] *Canals and Inland Waterways. Report of the Board of Survey*, B.T.C., London (1955).
[2] *Report of the Committee of Inquiry into Inland Waterways*. H.M.S.O. Cmd. 486 (1958).
[3] Certain other undertakings showed profits, such as the Ashton Canal, but these were due to large receipts from sources other than traffic. Report (1955) *supra*, Appendix 3.
[4] ibid., Appendix 6.

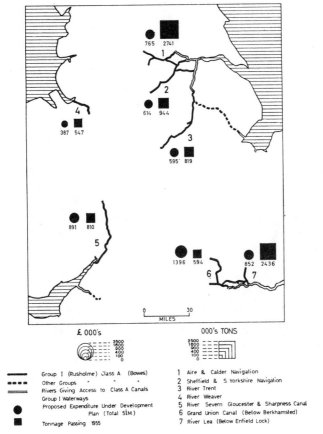

FIG. 41. THE DEVELOPMENT PLAN FOR GROUP I WATERWAYS

Source: W. L. Ives, 'The Problem of our Inland Waterways'. London. B.T.C., 1957

the explanation: apart from the section of the Grand Union Canal all the Group I waterways are either navigable rivers or cuts made through level alluvial lowlands or valley-bottoms. They occur in physiographic situations of a type so common in northern Germany, the Netherlands, and Belgium that these countries are able to make far more use of water transport than is possible in Britain. In common with these continental canals also they possess the property of being able to accommodate large barges. For instance 400-ton barges can reach Winsford on the Weaver and Worcester on the Severn. Some of the more important improvements at present under construction or recently completed are aimed· at increasing accessibility still further. The Cromwell Lock on the Trent and the Sandall Lock (Plate 37) on the Sheffield & South Yorkshire will have this effect.

To the 380 miles of Class A Waterway may be added the 935

Photo: Pickard (Leeds), by courtesy of British Transport Waterways

PLATE 37. LONG SANDALL NEW LOCK, YORKSHIRE

This is an example of a post-war undertaking aimed at the improvement of an important inland waterway. Its completion means that the Sheffield & South Yorkshire Navigation can now accommodate as far as Hexthorpe, above Doncaster, not only craft capable of carrying 250 tons, but also the trains of compartment-boats ('Tom Puddings') which are largely responsible for the cheapness of coal transport to Goole from collieries on this canal and the Aire & Calder Navigation. View to the south-south-west.

miles scheduled in the Bowes Report as Class B, the whole making up the 'Prescribed Navigable System', and it seems likely that these will have a further lease of life and do useful work, but ultimately the odds are against them. They are mostly narrow canals unable to accommodate barges of over 25 or 30 tons burden, and locks are often a serious problem. In many of these and the other canals· not included in the Prescribed Navigable System the issue of re-tention or closure is likely to be decided on grounds other than transport efficiency. These 'alien uses' such as the provision of water to industrial premises are sometimes far more important than the carrying of traffic. On the Monkland Canal water and other rents comprise the entire income since the canal is no longer open to navigation.

In this process of adjustment it will be noted that the long-distance trunk lines are no longer in the forefront of the canal system. Some, such as the main units in the 'cross', the diagonal links between Mersey, and Thames, Humber and Severn, are recommended for retention. Others, such as the Thames & Severn and Wilts & Berks, are already unnavigable as through routes. This is perhaps the most striking point of contrast between the canals and the railways. As a result of post-war developments the pattern of trunk railways which emerged in the middle of the last century, far from showing signs of breaking down, has been exaggerated by the elimination of numerous lesser units. The process is reminiscent of the pruning of a bush fruit-tree, in which the few selected 'leaders' are encouraged by the removal of the maze of smaller twigs.

The counterpart of the Development Plan for the waterways is the modernization programme for the railways announced at the end of 1954, though the scale of the project is incomparably larger.[5] It was planned to spend some £1,200 million over a fifteen-year period up to 1970. Much of this expenditure will be on items which will not greatly alter the railway map. For instance some £75 million was earmarked for the provision of continuous vacuum brakes on goods wagons and another £150 million for the replacement of obsolete by more modern wagons. But other parts of the programme carry geographical implications of a kind which can best be suggested by a few examples.

The relative status of the main lines as against the branch lines can be seen from the major track improvements which are envisaged under the plan. An important project, for instance, is the widening of the former Great Northern main line out of King's Cross. In order to maintain a ruling gradient of 1 in 200 and at the same time to keep to a reasonably direct line of route, it was necessary to use engineering works of considerable magnitude in crossing the Tertiaries and the Chalk of the London Basin. In particular many tunnels were required—no less than nine in the first twenty-four miles from King's Cross. Two tracks were provided,

[5] *Modernisation and Re-equipment of British Railways*, B.T.C. (1955).

but by the eighteen-eighties these were proving inadequate and extensive widening schemes were put in hand in 1882. Within ten years extra tunnels had been brought into use at Wood Green and Oakleigh Park, so that four tracks were available as far as New Barnet.[6] Already the Gasworks and Copenhagen tunnels in the immediate approaches to King's Cross were completed in triplicate, carrying six tracks in all. From 1885 onwards widening was also undertaken northwards towards Biggleswade, but at two points engineering difficulties prevented the completion of continuous four-track line. Between New Barnet and Potter's Bar three tunnels occur and further north, between Welwyn Garden City and Woolmer Green, the two Welwyn Tunnels and the Welwyn Viaduct presented further obstacles. When, sixty-two years after the completion of the widening to New Barnet, the modernization plan was announced, these two bottlenecks remained. The removal of the more southerly was particularly urgent, because, in addition to main-line traffic, it has to cope with a heavy suburban service which runs only as far as Welwyn Garden City, stopping short, that is to say, before the bottleneck on the Welwyn Viaduct. The quadrupling of this section from New Barnet to Potter's Bar involving the provision of second tunnels at Hadley Wood South, Hadley Wood North (Plate 38), and Potter's Bar, as well as the complete reconstruction of Potter's Bar Station, was therefore given a high order of priority.

Another example of a scheme for the elimination of bottlenecks is that which has been carried out on the main line of the former London, Chatham & Dover Railway. This route was mainly of double track,[7] but between Shortlands, where the 'Catford Loop' rejoins the main line, and Bickley, where traffic for Sevenoaks, Ashford, and Dover diverges, four tracks were available. This section is used not only by heavy suburban traffic and seaside traffic to north Kent, but also by boat-trains. Beyond Bickley the line narrowed again to double track, and this caused much congestion as far as Swanley Junction, where the Maidstone and Sevenoaks (via Otford) traffic diverges. This Bickley–Swanley section has therefore been quadrupled, and the opportunity has been taken virtually to rebuild the complicated junction at Bickley so as to allow much faster running over the points and curves. Further east, between Rainham and Newington, a further section

[6] C. H. Grinling, *The History of the Great Northern Railway* (1898), p. 415.
[7] 'Modernisation of the Kent Coast Main Line'. *Rly. Mag.* (May 1958), p. 311.

has been quadrupled to allow fast trains to overtake stopping trains.[8]

The urgency of this widening has been largely brought about by the extension of electrification in east Kent. Previously electrification ended at Gillingham, but the Ramsgate and Dover lines (together with the Sheerness branch) were scheduled for inclusion

Photograph by kind permission of the Eastern Region, British Railways, and the 'Railway Magazine'

PLATE 38. HADLEY NORTH TUNNELS, HERTFORDSHIRE

The quadrupling of the Great Northern main line between Potter's Bar and the Welwyn Viaduct was completed in May 1959. It necessitated the making of duplicate tunnels at Hadley South, Hadley North, and Potter's Bar. The photograph shows the southern portals of the old and new tunnels at Hadley North, carrying the line under a projecting finger of London Clay which separates the valleys of two right-bank tributaries of the River Lea. View to the north-north-west.

in the first stage of electrification in east Kent. This brings us to another aspect of the plan which is to have a profound effect on the railway map.

Generally speaking electric traction is a form of motive power cheap to operate but expensive to install. Consequently it can be justified only where the utilization of the line is high. This brings

[8] 'The Rainham–Newington Widening'. *Rly. Mag.* (Jan. 1958), p. 51.

into the picture two main kinds of railway, the trunk lines, carrying heavy traffic for long distances, and the suburban lines, carrying heavy traffic for short distances. In the Home Counties, and particularly in the sector between London and the South Coast, suburban traffic has now pushed out so far from London that it is increasingly difficult to distinguish between what is suburban and what is 'main line'. Furthermore before 1939 a far greater network of electrified line was to be found here than anywhere else in Britain. The electrification programme[9] therefore started with an existing network hereabouts employing the third-rail system, and although this was rejected as a method for general use in main-line electrification, it was recognized that development had gone so far that further electrification *in this area* must follow suit.

In other parts of the country the development of electrification with conductor-rail was so limited—it occurred only on Tyneside, in the Wirral, and south Lancashire—that it had no effect on the modernization plans, in which overhead contact was adopted as the standard method. The two big projects started by the L.N.E.R. for electrification between Liverpool Street and Shenfield (Essex) and between Manchester, Sheffield, and Wath-upon-Dearne, have been completed since the war, and the former, originally a purely suburban project, is now being extended along the main line to Ipswich and includes the Clacton, Walton, Harwich, and Felixstowe branches. Electrification has also been completed from Shenfield to Southend.

Here, then, will be a compact system carrying a fairly heavy traffic. Beyond Ipswich the density of traffic thins out considerably, as it is divided between the Norwich and Yarmouth lines, but at Ipswich the 'funnelling' effect begins to be felt and it is this which will provide the train-frequency adequate to justify electrification.

The largest electrification projects under the plan concern the main lines from Euston and King's Cross. The Euston line is to be electrified as far as Liverpool and Manchester, including the north Staffordshire approach to Manchester through the Potteries, and the loop from Rugby to Stafford via Coventry, Birmingham, and Wolverhampton, and several other short lines in the West Midlands. The East Coast main line will be electrified to Leeds. The Doncaster–York section was included in the plan as a 'possible', and now seems to be a 'certainty'.

[9] *The System of Electrification for British Railways*, B.T.C. (n.d.)

The outcome of this electrification, therefore, will be to emphasize still further the importance of these two trunk routes as arteries in the railway system of the country. Very different will be the Clydeside electrification, which, apart from some schemes in the northern part of the Home Counties, will complete the electrification up to 1970.[10] This will be an essentially suburban electrification. The main line to London will not be affected in the first instance beyond Motherwell, but altogether about a dozen lines leading out of Glasgow as far as Wemyss Bay, Helensburgh, Milngavie, and Airdrie will be electrified.

The modernization plan will not involve the construction of any long sections of new route. It will, however, include the provision of short lengths of new track to enhance the value of existing railways for specific purposes. Probably the most important of these schemes, and one which has been given high priority, is the Oxford–Cambridge line, which has been earmarked for development as a through freight route.[11] The number of wagons transferred between Regions of British Railways in the London area is of the order of 10,000 per day and it was anticipated that much of this interchange, with its attendant congestion, could be eliminated by the improvement of cross-country facilities between main lines outside the London area.

Another way in which the plan will profoundly affect the railway map is to be found in the location of marshalling yards. The existing yards

. . . reflect a system of routing designed to ensure that the company that accepted the traffic could keep it on its own system for the longest possible distance, and were not specially designed to facilitate through working. . . . Rational methods of operating, based on the use of facilities without regard to previous company ownership, require the elimination of many of these old yards and their replacement by a smaller number of modern yards. . . . The plan provides for the construction or re-construction of some fifty-five marshalling yards, which would result in the total or partial closure of about 150 existing yards.[12]

Some idea of the sort of issues which lie behind the re-siting of marshalling yards may be obtained from the yard at Thornton, Fife (Fig. 42). This yard has been built to handle by the most up-to-date techniques traffic previously dealt with 'in six yards or

[10] According to the original programme. Subsequent events suggest that this may be accelerated.

[11] 'London Bypass Route for Freight Traffic'. *Rly. Mag.* (Feb. 1958), p. 95.

[12] *Modernisation and Re-equipment of British Railways*, B.T.C. (1955), pp. 21–22.

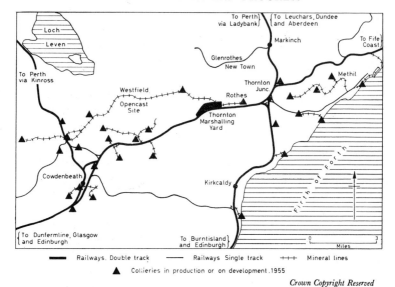

FIG. 42. THORNTON MARSHALLING YARD AND RAIL
CONNEXIONS, FIFE

Collieries from 'The Colliery Guardian, Guide to the Coalfields', 1956

groups of sidings near Thornton Station, and in four at Burnt-island, Townhill (near Dumfermline), and Methil'.[13] The geographical background is that of an established coalfield undergoing or about to undergo vigorous new development. Coal will be by far the most important commodity handled, and the Thornton yard will be the principal link between production sites and lines of communication out of the area.

The main traffic flows from the yard are northwards via the Tay Bridge to Dundee, Aberdeen and so on; northwards via Perth to points south and north of Inverness, and to Inverness itself; and westwards to Glasgow and the West of Scotland. At present, the volume of traffic in each flow is roughly equal.[14]

The railways best situated to handle this traffic converge on Thornton, which is also situated on the direct line north-eastwards from the Forth Bridge.

The relation between the yard and the coal-producing sites finds expression both in its general centrality within the coalfield and in its more immediate connexion with particular sites. Thus

[13] 'Thornton Marshalling Yard, Scottish Region'. *Rly. Mag.* (Feb. 1958), p. 129.
[14] ibid., p. 130.

one of the largest of the N.C.B.'s new pits, the Rothes Colliery, is only a mile from the yard and has direct entry to it by its own line. On the other side (west) another mineral line connects the yard with the vast open-cast site at present being developed at West-field.

While the situation in relation to railway routes and production sites is of paramount importance, other factors have been taken into consideration in selecting the site. These include

. . . the location of the homes of staff, the possibility of mining subsi-dence, the need to avoid interference with traffic working during construction, the position of the existing motive power depot at Thornton and . . . the density, direction, and future development of passenger services. . . .[15]

Unfortunately by far the most apparent effect which recent developments have had on the railway map has been to secure a large diminution in the total mileage open. It is equally unfortun-ate that public attention has been focused mainly on this aspect. The process of recession may take place in various degrees. It may merely take the form of diminution of traffic or of the frequency, speed, and efficiency of particular services. It may mean the closing of stations on lines which retain their importance for long-distance traffic. (The Euston–Carlisle line would furnish numerous ex-amples.) It may mean the withdrawal of passenger but not goods services. It may mean the total withdrawal of services with pro-vision for the maintenance of track, or, in the last resort, the total abandonment of the line.

It is erroneous to regard this as an exclusively post-war issue. Recession has always gone on hand in hand with expansion. As far as passenger lines are concerned Greville and Spence[16] have shown the magnitude of recession up to the time of the Second World War. But the cumulative effect of competition from road transport and the necessity and opportunity for modernization have accelerated the pace. For instance, the closure of railways in the Whitby area illustrates the way in which abandonment (of the Whitby–Loftus line) has been phased with the programme of con-version to diesel traction on the alternative route between Whitby and Teesside.[17] It must be accepted that the elimination of some

[15] ibid., p. 129.
[16] M. D. Greville and Jeoffry Spence, *A Handbook to Closed Passenger Lines in England and Wales, 1827 to 1939* (1955).
[17] J. H. Appleton, 'Communications'. *A Survey of Whitby*, ed. G. H. J. Daysh (1958), p. 238.

Photo: E. L. Wilson

PLATE 39. THE PELHAM STREET BRIDGE, LINCOLN

The railways of Lincoln, converging on the low-lying alluvium which flanks the Witham, form a barrier which has almost cut off the southern part of the city from the old centre.

Two thoroughfares only cross this barrier. The more westerly, the High Street, leading right into the city centre, has two level-crossings which greatly aggravate the congestion. Most of the through traffic, therefore, has for some time been routed along the more easterly, Pelham Street. This street crossed the railways at a point where they crossed each other! The photograph shows the position of the former level-crossing and the new bridge by which the railway-barrier is now spanned. View to the south.

unprofitable lines is as much a part of the adjustment to changing conditions as are the more positive adaptations of those sections which are being 'tuned up' for the essential part which they will continue to play in the country's communications. It is simply a fact that the balance between road and rail transport has been altered, and it would be very remarkable if this were not reflected in the map. The influence which this is about to have on the road-pattern, though not necessarily greater, is in many ways more spectacular, in that it implies the construction of some entirely new elements, some of them on a scale unprecedented in this country.

Photo: Aerofilms

PLATE 40. THE CHISWICK FLY-OVER

One of the most important urban road-building projects is that which is aimed at improving access into Central London from the West. This is being undertaken in several phases. The Cromwell Road Extension and the Chiswick Fly-over (shown here) are the two most important features at the inner end. Westwards from the fly-over the road is to be continued to the new Slough–Maidenhead By-pass, partly on viaduct over the Great West Road. The whole thoroughfare is designed to improve communications with London Airport as well as to form part of the South Wales Radial Motorway. The principal roads converging on the fly-over are the Great West Road (right foreground), Gunnersbury Avenue (left foreground), Chiswick High Road (left centre), and the reconstructed Cedars Road (top left). View to the south-east.

Even so it is necessary to see these developments as part of the process of adaptation described in a previous chapter (VI). It is universally agreed that the volume of road traffic has outgrown the capacity of the road network, but this has not happened evenly, and consequently the location of those points or areas where relief is most urgent has largely dominated the programme. Although the difficulties encountered in each one of these areas are peculiar to it, one does find certain kinds of situation into which the majority of projects fall. First there are the urban areas and their immediate environs. Secondly there are those important roads (not necessarily all 'trunk' roads in the Ministry's classification) whose capacity is inadequate for their traffic. Many miles of road in this category are being widened without necessarily being laid out in new alignments. Thirdly, where this type of improvement is insufficient, entirely new motorways are being built, and fourthly, as a special case, new road communications are being opened up by the crossing of estuaries hitherto regarded as economically impassable.

Some of the urban schemes are concerned with the relief of internal traffic problems in town centres. The Pelham Bridge in Lincoln, for instance, was built to eliminate the level-crossings which blocked the main traffic route just to the east of the stations (Plate 39). Major widening schemes have been undertaken in London, such as in Notting Hill Gate, Cheapside, and the Strand. A new road has had to be provided in an area of heavy post-war reconstruction in the City between Aldersgate Street and Moorgate, and the whole road-system at the Elephant and Castle has been replanned. The inner approaches from the Great West Road (A.4) have been re-modelled (Plate 40). Work on inner ring roads has been going on in several cities, such as Southampton, Sheffield, Birmingham, and Nottingham, and the elimination of urban congestion by new by-passes accounts for much of the mileage of recently built roads. Examples from the Midlands, for instance, include Thurmaston (Leicestershire), Halesowen (Worcestershire), Borrowash (Derbyshire), Meriden and Dunchurch (Warwickshire), East Retford (Nottinghamshire), and Stone (Staffordshire). The eastern and western by-passes in Oxford are about to complete a through-traffic scheme of which the inter-war by-passes around the northern and southern sides of the town formed only a first part. New by-passes are in evidence, too, on the main radial roads from London in the Home Counties, such as in Hertfordshire at Markyate (A.5) and Colney (A.6), in Kent at Ashford and Maidstone (Plate 26), and in Essex at Harlow (A.11), Ingatestone (A.12), and East Ham and Barking (A.15). The construction of the Stretford–Eccles By-pass, which is in effect the orbital road round the western side of Manchester, involves the bridging of the Manchester Ship Canal by the high-level bridge at Barton (Plate 41).

In most of these instances important through routeways are concerned, and the relief of local urban congestion is merely a part of the process of trunk road improvement. Much of this programme

Photo: Aerofilms

PLATE 41. BARTON HIGH-LEVEL BRIDGE UNDER CONSTRUCTION

Note the length of the bridge-approaches necessitated by the height at which the canal has to be spanned. In the distance can be seen the low-level swing bridge carrying the Stretford–Eccles road (A.575) and immediately beyond it the Barton Aqueduct (Bridgewater Canal); which is in the open position. View to the east-north-east.

of improvement is taking the form of widening, sometimes, as on parts of the Great North Road, by the building of a second carriageway parallel with the earlier road, which then becomes one element in a dual-carriageway system. Nearly all of the Great North Road between London and Newcastle is scheduled for conversion to dual carriageway without any serious changes in the alignment except where by-passes are being built, as at Wetherby and Catterick.

Improvements in existing roads, however, cannot alone provide Britain with an adequate road-system and several entirely new motorways, from which all other kinds of traffic will be excluded, are being provided. These motorways are intended to connect the great industrial centres of England and Wales by means of a network as economical in mileage as is consistent with traffic requirements. Thus London is being linked with the Bristol area

G.C.—Q

and South Wales by the South Wales Radial Road, and with the Midlands by the London to Birmingham Motorway.[18] But for more distant destinations in Lancashire and Yorkshire the cost of providing separate motorways direct from London would be prohibitive at present, so the Birmingham route will act as a common trunk as far as Watford Gap or Crick some six miles south-east of Rugby, where the separation of the eastern and western motorways will take place. It is interesting to note that this is precisely what happened in the early days of railways, when the London & Birmingham fulfilled a similar function as far as Rugby. In railway history this compromise lasted for about a decade before the direct London–Doncaster route abstracted the East Coast traffic. One wonders how long the arrangement will be adequate for the motorways. There is, of course, no precise parallel, since the improved Great North Road will be available to play the role equivalent to that of the Great Northern Railway.

Another motorway is to link Birmingham with Bristol and South Wales, dividing a little to the north of Tewkesbury. One section of this scheme, known as the Ross Spur, was among the earliest pieces of motorway to be commenced. This was intended to effect an immediate and urgent improvement in a traffic-flow (between the Midlands and South Wales) which has greatly increased in volume since the war, while at the same time anticipating the eventual completion of a larger scheme of which it will form a part. A similar purpose lies behind the Preston (Plate 42) and Lancaster by-passes commenced in 1956 and 1957 respectively. They will eventually form a northern extension of the London to Lancashire motorway link.

The Channel Ports Motorway is aimed at providing a greatly improved approach road to London from Dover via Canterbury. The present A.2 road is quite inadequate for this purpose. The towns of Strood, Rochester, Chatham, Gillingham, Sittingbourne, and Faversham have collectively created such a problem that local by-pass schemes are impracticable, and a new section of motorway, leaving the present road just west of Strood, will pass well up the dipslope of the North Downs, reaching 600 feet near Bredhurst, and will cut out the whole of this section of road. In

---

[18] *London–Yorkshire Motorway; first section,* H.M.S.O. (1959). I am indebted for much information on this and other schemes to Mr. S. W. Bainbridge and Mr. W. F. Adams of the Ministry of Transport.

Photo: Aerofilms

PLATE 42. THE PRESTON BY-PASS

Completed in 1958, the Preston By-pass was the first section of motorway to be brought into operation in Britain. The picture shows the crossing of the Ribble and the Samlesbury Fly-over by which the motorway crosses the Preston–Clitheroe road (A.59). View to the east.

spite of the new by-pass construction at Maidstone and Ashford on the alternative Dover road (A.20), the motorway is being given high priority.

Other motorways are envisaged by the Ministry of Transport and the future programme will include an orbital road round the northern side of London. It has been allowed for, for instance, in the plans for Harlow New Town (Fig. 22), and the western portion of the Staines By-pass will form a part of it. These motorways aim at achieving standards of design which have not previously been reached in this country except in quite short sections of road. A width of 24 feet for each of the two carriageways has been adopted for general use, but greater widths will be used where the expectation of traffic demands, for instance, 36 feet on the main part of the London to Birmingham Motorway. Intersections with existing roads will be strictly limited. The early plans suggest an average interval of about six miles between road intersections. All other crossings of existing roads will be made by under- or over-bridges. In order to find a route permitting the necessary standards through some of the urban areas, enterprising new techniques of construction will be called for, such as the 'double-decker' road near Brentford, where the South Wales Radial is to be carried on viaduct over the present Great West Road. Other proposals at present include the building of a three-mile motorway viaduct over the railway through Smethwick and Oldbury in order to find a way through the built-up area between Birmingham and Wolverhampton, and the carrying of a motorway for a mile and a quarter over a culvert in which the River Tame will run.

One of the most important geographical consequences of post-war road construction plans will be the crossing of major estuaries much further downstream than hitherto. As has been pointed out in Chapter III the tendency has been for the larger estuaries to be crossed by railways lower down than the lowest road-crossings. However, the Thames has long been an exception, thanks to the Rotherhithe and Blackwall tunnels, and in the nineteen-thirties the Mersey road tunnel joined the earlier railway tunnel between Liverpool and Birkenhead. The lowest road bridge, however, was at Warrington, apart from the freak transporter bridge at Runcorn (Plate 16). The replacement of this by a modern road bridge was started in 1956.

The same year saw the completion of the bridge over the River Neath in Glamorgan, which, although only some two miles lower down, eliminated one of the worst stretches of urban congestion at the earlier bridgehead in the town of Neath.

To the Rotherhithe and Blackwall tunnels a third is now being added between Dartford and Purfleet which will make possible the by-passing of London on its eastern side without the inconvenience of a ferry crossing. The present tunnels are situated so far upstream that traffic using them is brought well within the built-up area of London.

Other tunnelling projects include the proposed Tyne tunnel between Jarrow and Howdon and the tunnel now under construction across the lower Clyde. All these schemes will be dwarfed if anything comes of the current revival of interest in the proposed Channel Tunnel, but plans at present are not sufficiently definite to warrant a full discussion here of this exciting project.

The ideology of post-war planning threw up several bridging schemes on the grand scale, and two of these are now approaching reality. The Firth of Forth not only penetrates more deeply than any other river into central Scotland, but also splits what is in effect a single coalfield into two separate parts. The development of the more northerly part, the Fifeshire Coalfield, is accentuating the need to replace the Queen's Ferry by a bridge (Plate 18). At present the lowest road bridge is a modern structure at Kincardine, and although its construction greatly improved access to Fife, the distance from Edinburgh to, say, Dunfermline, is still about 25 miles longer than via the ferry and the roads are decidedly slow in places.

The other scheme, that for bridging the Severn, will be an essential part of the South Wales Radial Road. The site selected is between Beachley and Aust. The Severn is here considerably narrower than at the railway tunnel further downstream, but the site is to be just above the point where the river is joined by the Wye and this has to be crossed by a separate bridge. It is estimated that there will be a saving of about fifty miles between Bristol and Cardiff as against the journey via Gloucester. The heavy concentrations of population and the recent expansion of new industries on both sides of the estuary have contributed to the urgency of this project.

The Forth and Severn Bridges will have much in common. Their designs are similar; they are both to be suspension bridges with main spans of almost equal length—3,300 feet for the Forth Bridge, 3,240 feet for the Severn. These will be the longest spans outside the United States and are expected to be respectively the fourth and fifth longest in the world. Both bridges will improve access to coalfields and expanding industrial areas and both will be financed by tolls. Proposals for a Tay road bridge, about a mile east of the railway bridge, have been approved in principle by the Secretary of State for Scotland.

Another project of similar design to the Forth and Severn Bridges but considerably further from realization is that which has been proposed for crossing the Humber. According to the plans of 1955 the site would be between Hessle and Barton, where the estuary is narrowed at its crossing of the outcrop of the Chalk. It is unfortunate that, among the arguments brought forward to urge the necessity for this bridge, are many which are spurious, such as, for instance, that it would provide an improved route between London and the North-east Coast. A glance at the map will show that this is just nonsense, and it will be even more so when the

London to Yorkshire Motorway is completed. Unrealistic arguments of this kind only serve to weaken a case which, on more local grounds, is very much stronger, and there is no doubt that the bridge would be a great convenience for the port of Hull. It would, incidentally, if built to the latest design, give this country a span 300 feet longer than the 4,200-foot span of the Golden Gate, the longest in the world when the Humber Bridge plans were drawn up.

The changing conditions of the post-war world have brought about some remarkable developments in pipeline construction. Two of the most striking examples will illustrate the significance of this form of transport in the economic geography of today.

As early as 1924 Scottish Oils Limited, a company interested in working the oil-shales on the south side of the Forth, opened an oil refinery at Grangemouth. The site, at the eastern end of the Forth & Clyde Canal, was accessible from the firth for tankers up to about 12,000 tons. There is no reason to regard the location of the refinery in relation to supplies of crude oil, markets, and labour supply as anything but reasonable. Since then, however, the size of tankers has enormously increased. The British Petroleum Company (which now controls the refinery) has on order sixteen tankers for delivery between 1960 and 1963 ranging in carrying capacity between 50,000 and 65,000 tons. Already much of the crude oil coming to this country is brought in vessels which could never get into Grangemouth Docks, and to meet this situation the Company constructed, between May 1950 and May 1951, a jetty at Finnart on Loch Long[19] with a pipeline right across the 'waist' of Scotland to the Grangemouth refinery. This pipeline of $12\frac{3}{4}$-inch external diameter has an annual capacity of $3\frac{1}{4}$ million tons, or roughly an eighth of the crude oil at present imported into Britain. With a working pressure of 1,000 lb. per square inch the pipeline is not confined to a level course, and this means that, by rising to a summit level of 640 feet, it can cross the hillier country to the north of Glasgow instead of having to follow the route of the Forth & Clyde Canal by the Clyde estuary and the Kelvin–Bonny Gap. The construction of the pipeline has had vital consequences for both the West and the East coasts. What is virtually a new port has arisen at Finnart on a site wholly admirable from the point of view of its sea-approach but physiographically quite unsuitable on its landward side for the development of 'conventional' com-

[19] *British Petroleum's Finnart Ocean Terminal.* B.P. explanatory booklet (1958).

munications. At the same time it is no exaggeration to say that the pipeline has made possible the persistence and expansion of the refinery on the Grangemouth site.

An enormous programme of pipeline construction has been carried out in the gas industry, which, as far as distribution is concerned, has been more radically affected by the social and economic changes of the post-war period than any other industry. The structure of the industry before vesting-day was such that the supply of gas tended to be made on an independent, local basis, with separate undertakings operating their own, isolated systems. Movement by pipeline occurred in the more densely populated areas, such as the Yorkshire–Nottinghamshire–Derbyshire Coalfield on quite a large scale, especially if surpluses of gas were available as industrial by-products. But there was no development of a comprehensive grid comparable with that in the electricity industry. Nationalization brought under the control of regional boards the whole problem of production and distribution over much larger areas than those previously served by even the largest undertakings, and this revolution in management created the opportunity for a fundamentally different approach to the question of production and distribution. The achievements of the South Western Board during the first ten years or so following nationalization will illustrate how far-reaching have been the consequences as far as the transport of gas is concerned.

The policy of the Board was to reduce the 105 separate gasworks (operated by 104 separate undertakings) to sixteen permanent manufacturing stations.[20] This meant that most of the separate existing networks, hitherto supplied by their own works, would have to be supplied by transporting gas by pipeline from elsewhere. In other words a trunk system or grid had to be constructed. Between 1 May 1949 and 31 March 1958, the mileage of mains in the area increased by 31·1 per cent. (from 4,313 to 5,654).[21] Much of this mileage was accounted for by new trunk mains, so that the effect on the map was far greater than the figure of 31·1 per cent. would suggest. The extent of the change can be seen in Figure 43. In 1949 there was scarcely any development of a trunk system south-west of Glastonbury, and in the north-eastern part the four main networks, centred on Gloucester–Cheltenham, Swindon,

[20] C. H. Chester, 'The Organization of the Gas Industry in the South West'. *Inst. Gas Eng., Publication No. 442* (1954).
[21] *South Western Gas Board. Annual Report and Accounts* (1957–8), p. 6.

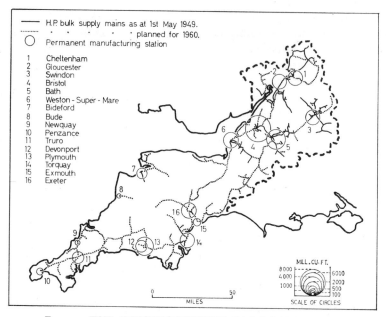

FIG. 43. THE SOUTH-WESTERN GAS BOARD AREA

Source: C. H. Chester. 'The organization of the gas industry in the South West.' Inst. of Gas Engineers, Publication No. 442, 1954; and South Western Gas Board, Reports and Accounts, Annual

Bristol–Bath, and Weston-super-Mare, were still separate. Yet within ten years (by October 1958) a continuous system of mains linked Evesham with Penzance.

Post-war developments in the transmission of electricity have been no less important, though perhaps they seem less revolutionary, thanks to the more extensive and ubiquitous pre-war growth of the 132-kV Grid, which, by 1939, already formed a fairly comprehensive network of high-voltage transmission lines. Here again the general patterns and trends of regional economic geography provide the background, though they must be coupled with the technical mastery of transmission at still higher voltages. In 1951 Rawstron wrote:

The ability to transmit electricity efficiently over distances formerly considered impossible, and the marked upward trend in the cost of coal transport combine to emphasize the importance of the general national demand as distinct from local demands in the siting of new stations.[22]

The most important event, therefore, from our point of view,

[22] E. M. Rawstron, 'The distribution and location of steam-driven power stations in Great Britain'. *Geography*, xxxvi (1951), p. 249.

has been the construction during this decade of a new Grid system, the 'Supergrid', designed to transmit current at 275 kV. Whereas the 132-kV Grid was 'initially designed to economise capital investment by reducing the amount of standby plant required and to increase economy by ensuring that at all times of the day the load was carried by the most efficient power stations',[23] the Supergrid is intended to '. . . make possible the transmission to London and other big towns of bulk supplies of electricity provided by a number of new power stations near the East Midlands coalfield'.[24]

The Supergrid therefore forms a fairly compact figure in the centre of the country. From Staythorpe, near Newark, a main line runs to Elstree (Hertfordshire) from which further distribution in the Home Counties takes place. Northwards from Staythorpe the main line leads through the West Riding to Tyneside, Carlisle, and the Clyde, and a westerly arm up the Trent valley by Castle Donington to Drakelow (near Burton) divides there for south Lancashire and the West Midlands respectively. Further lines are under construction between the Midlands and the South.

However, no sooner had this policy of siting power stations on the East Midland Field (with its advantages of centrality, cooling water from the Trent, and high efficiency in the coal industry) been accepted as practicable, than the appearance of atomic power stations began to suggest a further modification for the future. Already it is possible to foresee a ring of coastal power stations which must eventually be linked with interior consuming centres by high-voltage lines following new directions and forming new and unfamiliar patterns on the map.

So it goes on. There have been periods when particular kinds of communications were appearing in the landscape no less rapidly. But taking the transport picture as a whole and considering abandonment and recession as well as construction and growth, there has never been a time when the process of adaptation was so vigorous, so far-reaching, and so deeply affected by revolutionary changes as at present. In one sense, therefore, this is the worst possible time to attempt a geographical analysis of the subject. It is like trying to paint a model who won't sit still. On the other hand the very fact that we are living in one of the great formative periods in the evolution of our communications may be taken as a reason for pausing to try and understand more about it.

[23] 'The Grid and Supergrid'. *Giant Power* (Oct. 1951), p. 8.   [24] ibid.

LIST OF ABBREVIATIONS

Railway Companies:

C.L.C.	Cheshire Lines Committee
G. & S.W.	Glasgow & South Western
G.N.R.	Great Northern
G.W.R.	Great Western
L. & Y.	Lancashire & Yorkshire
L.M.S.R.	London, Midland & Scottish
L.N.E.R.	London & North Eastern
L.N.W.R.	London & North Western
L.S.W.R.	London & South Western
M. & G.N.	Midland & Great Northern
M.R.	Midland
M.S. & L.	Manchester, Sheffield & Lincolnshire
N.E.R.	North Eastern

Other Abbreviations:

B.T.C.	British Transport Commission
G.J.	*Geographical Journal*
I.B.G.	Institute of British Geographers
I.C.I.	Imperial Chemical Industries
N.C.B.	National Coal Board
O.D.	Ordnance Datum
O.S.	Ordnance Survey
P.G.A.	*Proceedings of the Geologists' Association*
Q.J.G.S.	*Quarterly Journal of the Geological Society*
S.G.M.	*Scottish Geographical Magazine*

THE NOMENCLATURE OF BRITISH RAILWAY COMPANIES

In the description of particular railways reference is often made to the names of the owning companies. A common difficulty arises from the fact that in Britain changes of ownership and changes of name have been frequent occurrences. Consequently one may have occasion to use one of several different names in referring to the same line at different dates. For instance the Blackburn, Darwen & Bolton Railway, incorporated in 1845, became in 1847 a part of the Bolton, Blackburn, Clitheroe & West Yorkshire Railway. In 1858 it became a part of the Lancashire & Yorkshire Railway which became a part of the London & North Western Railway in 1922. The following year this company in turn became a part of the London, Midland & Scottish Railway which in 1948 became a part of the London Midland Region of British Railways. There are thus six names which at various dates could properly be applied to this short section of line between Bolton and Blackburn.

These changes were part of the gradual process of consolidation which went on throughout the second half of the nineteenth century and the first part of the twentieth, and which resulted in most of the mileage of railways in Britain passing into the hands of about two dozen large companies. After the First World War a scheme of compulsory amalgamation brought nearly all of these companies into one of four main groups. These amalgamations, known colloquially as 'the Grouping', were carried out under the authority of the Railways Act, 1921, and came into effect as from 1 January 1923. The principal constituent companies of the four groups were as follows:

London, Midland & Scottish Railway
    London & North Western Railway (including the recently
        amalgamated Lancashire & Yorkshire)
    Midland Railway
    North Staffordshire Railway
    Furness Railway
    Caledonian Railway
    Glasgow & South Western Railway
    Highland Railway
        together with some twenty-six subsidiaries

London & North Eastern Railway
    North Eastern Railway (including the Hull & Barnsley Railway,
      amalgamated in 1922)
    Great Central Railway
    Great Eastern Railway
    Great Northern Railway
    Great North of Scotland Railway
    North British Railway
      together with twenty-six subsidiaries

Great Western Railway
    Great Western Railway
    Cambrian Railway
    Five medium-sized companies in South Wales
      together with twenty-seven subsidiaries

Southern Railway
    London & South Western Railway
    London, Brighton & South Coast Railway
    South Eastern & Chatham Railway
      together with seventeen subsidiaries

A large number of small companies found themselves jointly owned by two of the 'Big Four' and many others remained separate, though these were all small local railways with the exception of the Metropolitan Railway and the London Underground Group.

This grouping of the railways remained in force for exactly a quarter of a century. On 1 January 1948, nationalization brought them all under the British Transport Commission. The present six Regions of British Railways reflect in many ways the historical continuity of ownership, but in some important respects earlier units have been broken up in an effort to create administrative divisions which are areas in the territorial sense, whereas previous divisions tended to be in the form of interpenetrating linear members, as one would expect from the slow growth of separate, competing companies.

The present London Midland Region is based on the English part of the L.M.S.R. while the Eastern and North-eastern Regions derive mainly from the L.N.E.R. The Western and Southern Regions are approximately the successors of the G.W.R. and S.R. respectively, while the Scottish Region comprises those parts of the L.M.S.R. and L.N.E.R. which lie north of the Border, but there is no precise correlation between any of the 'Big Four' and any of the present Regions.

In addition to the names of these various companies the reader will encounter the terms 'East Coast main line' and 'West Coast main line' which are used to denote the principal trunk lines of railway between London and Scotland. They became established under the ownership of more than one company and are at present administered under more than one Region.

The East Coast main line until 1923 was owned by the Great Northern Railway from London (King's Cross) as far as Shaftholme Junction, north of Doncaster (160 miles). From there to Berwick-on-Tweed (175 miles) the line passed through York and Newcastle and was the property of the North Eastern Railway. The remaining portion (58 miles) to Edinburgh (Waverley) was owned by the North British Railway whose system stretched further west to Glasgow (Queen Street), Fort William and Mallaig, and north-east to Dundee and Kinnaber Junction (near Montrose), beyond which it exercised running powers to Aberdeen.

The West Coast main line from London (Euston) via Rugby, Crewe, and Preston was under the control of the London & North Western Railway as far as Carlisle, and was continued to Glasgow (Central) and Edinburgh (Prince's Street, from Carstairs Junction) by the Caledonian Railway, which also extended to Perth, Aberdeen, and the Western Highlands.

In 1923 the East and West Coast main lines passed wholly into the hands of the L.N.E.R. and L.M.S.R. respectively, but on nationalization in 1948 they again became divided between different Regions of British Railways. The English section of the East Coast main line was divided between the Eastern and North-eastern Regions, while that of the West Coast main line became part of the London Midland Region. The Scottish sections of both routes came under the Scottish Region.

A third route to Scotland was provided by the Midland Railway between London (St. Pancras) and Carlisle, and this became associated with the Glasgow & South Western and the North British routes from Carlisle to Glasgow (St. Enoch) and Edinburgh (Waverley) respectively.

CLASSIFICATIONS OF CANALS

The Rusholme Report (*Canals and Inland Waterways. Report of the Board of Survey*. B.T.C., 1955) divided the canals controlled by the Commission into three groups. Those in Group I were recommended for development, those in Group II for retention. All others were placed in Group III and their retention for navigation was not felt to be justified.

The Bowes Report (*Report of the Committee of Inquiry into Inland Waterways*. H.M.S.O., 1958) distinguished two Classes (A and B) which together were recommended to make up the 'Prescribed Navigable System'. All others were to be dealt with under specially prepared schemes to meet particular requirements.

The apportioning of the canals of England and Wales to these Groups and Classes was as follows:

	Rusholme Group
THE PRESCRIBED NAVIGABLE SYSTEM (Bowes)	

Class A (Bowes)

Aire & Calder Navigation (including Lower Ouse Improvement)	I
Gloucester & Berkeley Canal and River Severn	I
Grand Union (Regent's Canal Dock and Brentford to Berkhamsted)	I
Sheffield & S. Yorkshire Navigation	I
R. Lea (below Enfield Lock)	I
R. Trent	I
R. Weaver	I
Fossdyke Canal	II
Kennet & Avon (Avon Section)	II
R. Witham	III

Class B (Bowes)

Ashby Canal (used section)	II
Birmingham Canal Navigations	II
Calder & Hebble Navigation	II
Coventry Canal	II
Grand Union Canal (above Berkhamsted)	II
Kensington Canal	II
R. Lea (above Enfield Lock) and R. Stort	II

Leeds & Liverpool Canal	II
Oxford Canal (northern section)	II
Oxford Canal (southern section)	III
St. Helen's Canal	II
Shropshire Union Canal (main line)	II
Stourbridge & Stourbridge Extension Canals	II
Stratford-on-Avon Canal (northern section)	II
Trent & Mersey Canal	II
Worcester & Birmingham Canal	II†

† All other canals owned by British Waterways in England and Wales were excluded from the Prescribed Navigable System. All were placed in Group III (Rusholme) except for the Ure Navigation (Group II) and the Staffordshire & Worcestershire Canal, which was proposed for inclusion in Group II as an alternative to the Worcester & Birmingham Canal.

SELECTED BIBLIOGRAPHY

There is no single book specifically devoted to the geography of British communications, and published papers and articles on the subject are few. In attempting an interpretation of communications in their environment the reader's attention has frequently been directed as much towards this environment as towards the lines of communication themselves. Similarly any suggestions for further reading must direct him into several related fields. He will find an abundance of literature descriptive of the geographical environment which, however, has little to say directly about communications, and innumerable works which seem to deal with every aspect of roads, railways, canals, and other communications except those with which this book is concerned. By drawing information from these various sources and fitting it together the reader will find ample opportunity for pursuing investigations further along all the lines here outlined, but he must not expect to find that this has already been done for him. The following notes do not provide him with a comprehensive bibliography. They merely aim at suggesting the sort of material which is available.

Any useful bibliography must therefore give a place to works which deal with those aspects of physical and regional geography which have a bearing on routes of all kinds, even though they may not ostensibly purport to do so. There are several readable textbooks which explain the physical basis of the landscape. Sir Arthur Trueman, *Geology and Scenery in England and Wales*, Pelican (1949), and L. Dudley Stamp, *Britain's Structure and Scenery*, New Naturalist (1946), cover the technical background to the geomorphological points discussed here. Other basic textbooks on this aspect include R. F. Peel, *Physical Geography* (1952), S. W. Wooldridge and R. S. Morgan, *An Outline of Geomorphology* (2nd ed. 1959), P. Lake, *Physical Geography* (2nd ed. 1949), F. J. Monkhouse, *Principles of Physical Geography* (new impression 1958), A. A. Miller, *The Skin of the Earth* (1953), and Arthur Holmes, *Principles of Physical Geology* (1944). *The Scientific Study of Scenery*, first published in 1900 by J. E. Marr, is still worth reading.

There are some books which deal with special aspects of geomorphology, such as J. A. Steers, *The Coastline of England and Wales* (1946), and S. W. Wooldridge and D. L. Linton, *Structure, Surface and Drainage in South-east England* (1939, re-published 1955), but many of the important sources on physical geography are to be found in geographical periodicals, and several papers of this kind have been mentioned in the chapter references. It would be impossible to produce here a list sufficiently comprehensive to be useful.

Most regional geographies contain sections on communications, such as L. D. Stamp and S. H. Beaver, *The British Isles* (4th ed. 1954), *Great Britain: Essays in Regional Geography* edited by A. G. Ogilvie (1937), and E. G. Bowen, *Wales: a Physical, Historical and Regional Geography* (1957). Some of the regional handbooks published by the British Association have brief sections on the subject. Wilfred Smith, *An Economic Geography of Great Britain* (1949), deals with the economic approach.

The literature on Town and Country Planning also contains much local detail, often from the point of view of traffic. Plans and surveys published by local planning authorities are now becoming fairly numerous and in addition some technical literature on planning is helpful. *A Textbook of Town and Country Planning*, published by APRR (1950), has been quoted more than once. T. W. Freeman, *Geography and Planning* (1958), and L. B. Escritt, *Regional Planning* (1943), are also useful, the latter not least for its bibliography.

A. C. O'Dell, *Railways and Geography*, filled a long overdue need when it appeared in 1956, but its scope is world-wide, and the treatment of British examples is therefore limited. S. H. Beaver, 'Geography from a railway train', *Geography*, vol. 21 (1936), suggested a line of approach which would lend itself to application elsewhere but which has not yet been followed up.

In the field of historical geography historians, economic historians, geographers, and others have begun to interest themselves in communications, and a wide range of material is now available. Some of this is to be found in works dealing with more general historical topics. W. G. Hoskins, *The Making of the English Landscape* (1955), contains a section on communications, as do the four companion volumes, H. P. R. Finberg, *Gloucestershire* (1955), Roy Millward, *Lancashire* (1955), W. G. V. Balchin, *Cornwall* (1954), and W. G. Hoskins, *Leicestershire* (1957). J. B. Mitchell, *Historical Geography* (1954) (Teach Yourself Series), devotes a chapter to 'The Changing Geography of Transport', H. J. Fleure, *A Natural History of Man in Britain* (1951), has one on 'Communications and Transport', and H. C. Darby (ed.), *An Historical Geography of England before A.D. 1800* (1936), refers to the subject *passim*. The Victoria County Histories are mostly very disappointing from this point of view, though in the Leicestershire history (vol. III) (1955), P. Russell, *Roads*, A. T. Patterson, *Canals*, and J. Simmons, *Railways*, show what can be done in treating communications as an important element in local history.

Most historical works devoted wholly to communications deal with some limited aspect. Canals, roads, and railways each tend to have their own literature, and many authors confine themselves still further to the study of one local area, one period or one company. In the history of canals J. Priestley, *Inland Navigation and Railroads of Great Britain* (1831), is unique for its period. Not only has it served as an important source for all later writers, but also, since its approach is factual and descriptive, and since the growth of the canal system was virtually complete when it was written, it is still one of the best general geographical accounts of the canal system at almost its greatest extent. Among more modern works may be mentioned G. Cadbury and S. P. Dobbs, *Canals and Inland Waterways* (1929), W. E. Wilson, *Inland Waterways of Great Britain* (1939), and L. T. C. Rolt, *The Inland Waterways of England* (1950). Charles Hadfield, *British Canals* (1950), is an excellent historical account. L. A. Edwards, *Inland Waterways of Great Britain and Northern Ireland* (1950), primarily an itinerary and gazetteer of particular canals, is a fruitful source of reference for factual material.

On roads there are several general works, such as Sydney and Beatrice Webb, *English Local Government: The Story of the Highway* (1913), but some of the most useful confine their treatment to particular areas. Donald G. Moir, 'The Roads of Scotland', *S.G.M.* (1956-7), may be quoted. Several papers by G. B. Grundy have appeared in the *Archaeological Journal. Ancient Highways of Devon and Cornwall*, vol. 98 (1941), is a good example. Many local societies have published papers of this sort, such as Ronald Good, *The Old Roads of Dorset* (Dorset Nat. Hist. and Arch. Soc.) (1940). I. D. Margary, by restricting not only the area but also the period with which he deals, has produced a really detailed study in *Roman Ways in the Weald* (1948). He has subsequently expanded the geographical scope of his work in *Roman Roads in Britain* (1955-7).

The amount of literature on railways is becoming vast. Most of the larger railway companies have their histories recorded but the quality of these works is variable. E. T. MacDermot, *History of the Great Western Railway*, published in two volumes (1927 and 1931), is a model for this kind of work, accurate, comprehensive, and highly readable. W. W. Tomlinson, *The North Eastern Railway: its rise and development* (1914), is another admirable history. Others, such as F. S. Williams, *The Midland Railway* (1877), would today be regarded as romances rather than histories, but contain useful historical data behind a façade of Victorian chat. Some excellent concise histories of many of the smaller companies, such as the North London, the Taff Vale, the Hull & Barnsley, have been published by the Oakwood Press.

The bibliography in A. C. O'Dell, *Railways and Geography*, lists some of the main historical works available, but one would like to add two important works by H. G. Lewin, *Early British Railways* (1928), and *The Railway Mania and its Aftermath* (1936). The latter in particular presents a mass of factual material on the middle and late eighteen-forties in a form highly convenient for a geographical review. Since O'Dell's book was published, there have appeared the second volume of C. Hamilton Ellis, *British Railway History* (1959), and the first volume of George Dow, *The Great Central Railway* (1960). O. S. Nock, *The Great Northern Railway*, appeared in 1958, and Ernest Carter, *An Historical Geography of the Railways of the British Isles*, in the following year. The title of the latter is somewhat misleading—it is not an historical geography at all in the sense in which the term has come to be used.

Much technical information on railways is available in various works of reference, such as the *Railway Yearbook, Gradients of the British Main Line Railways* (both published by the Railway Publishing Co.), and *Railway Junction Diagrams*, published by the Railway Clearing House. *Bradshaw's Railway Guide* is indispensable, and *Bradshaw's Air Guide* may be mentioned here for convenience.

In addition to articles and papers in geographical and historical periodicals (e.g. T. J. Chandler, 'Communications and a coalfield', *I.B.G., Trans. & Papers*, 1957), there are several periodicals devoted wholly to transport and these contain many useful articles. *The Railway Magazine* in particular has many on historical and other topics. As an example one may cite two recent series by M. D. Greville and G. O. Holt on railway development in three Lancashire towns: Manchester (Sept.–Nov. 1957), Liverpool (Feb.–April 1959), and Preston (Feb.–April 1960). *The Railway Gazette* and *Modern Transport* are important publications and a comparatively recent venture, coming from the University of Leicester, is the *Journal of Transport History*.

From time to time Royal Commissions, etc., have published reports on various topics. Those of the commissioners for Highland Roads and Bridges, for instance, from 1803 to 1820, throw much light on a vital phase of road-making in Scotland, and there have been several reports on canals and railways.

Finally maps. These fall into two main categories. In the first are those maps the purpose of which is to show only or mainly communications. The Ordnance Survey has published *Roads* and *Railways* in the 'ten-mile' series of Great Britain, each in two sheets. Philips have produced a Railway Map of the British Isles coloured according to the 1921 Grouping, a feature also found in the reproduction of the Railway Clearing House maps by Ian Allan (1948). The same publisher has more recently produced a far more comprehensive *British Railways Pre-Grouping Atlas and Gazetteer* (1957), edited by W. P. Conolly. Many of the Tourist Road Atlases are also useful. The O.S. maps of Roman Britain and Seventeenth-Century Britain contain useful details of roads.

In the second category come those general topographical maps which depict lines of communication among other features of the landscape, and these, if properly used, can be an inexhaustible source of information, posing questions as well as suggesting answers, but giving a more complete picture of communications in their total environment than can be obtained from any other source except field observation.

Readers unaccustomed to map interpretation may turn to A. Garnett, *The Geographical Interpretation of Topographical Maps* (1930), G. H. Dury, *Map Interpretation* (1952), or D. Sylvester, *Map and Landscape* (1952). As for the maps themselves the Ordnance Survey one-inch maps (Seventh Series) and the 1 : 25,000 maps enable one to gain a fairly clear idea of where the roads, canals, and railways are. Armed with this equipment, those who wish to do so may proceed to face the question 'Why there?' Good luck to them!

INDEX

Note: Some subject-headings, such as 'Roads', 'Railways', etc., and some place-names, such as 'London', 'Scotland', etc., have been omitted from the Index on the grounds that references to them are so widely distributed throughout the book that no useful purpose would be served by their inclusion.